Every so ofte

Ahead of it. Behind. It doesn't matter. *"A real character"* people call them. *"A real book, that one."* You know someone like that. If you're lucky, you know a few. These extraordinary, ordinary people straddle the wobbly line between brilliance and madness, comedy and tragedy, success and failure. When they speak, it's poetry. It's in the air and then it's gone. Maybe it touches the lives of those within earshot. Maybe it's ignored altogether. Maybe it isn't even said out loud. Just a thought. A notion. A train of thoughts. **The Portrait Series** is an attempt to ride that train. It is an ongoing suite of narrative books that document and portray the stoop philosophers, sit-down comedians, and off-the-cuff bards who puncture the predictability of daily life.

claude

has lived as an artist, perennial student, underground doctor, philanthropist, homeless person, inventor, and entrepreneur. This intimate portrait of Claude Debs, an orphaned survivor of child sexual abuse turned fiercely independent citizen of the world, follows Claude's pilgrimage from the Middle East to France, Russia, and America. It traverses riotous experiences and offers heretical and searing observations on hyper-sexuality, marriage, lying, friendship, the art of alchemy, and hard-fought living.

claude

written and designed by

claude

warren lehrer

a narrative portrait of
claude debs

BAY PRESS SEATTLE

with photographs by jim frank & warren lehrer of

The Portrait Series
Claude

© 1995 Warren Lehrer *all rights reserved*
Bodyscape photographs by Warren Lehrer
Full-body photographs by Jim Frank and Warren Lehrer
This portrait is inspired by the life of Claude Debs.
The names of some people and institutions have been changed.
ISBN 0-941920-35-6
Library of Congress Card Number 95-5812
First printing 1995

Published by **Bay Press, Inc.**
115 West Denny Way, Seattle, Washington
9 8 1 1 9 . 4 2 0 5

The paper in this book meets the guidelines for permanence and durability
of the Committee on Production Guidelines for Book Longevity of the
Council on Library Resources. Printed in the Republic of Korea.

This book was made possible in part by a
New York State Council on the Arts Sponsored Artist Grant.

claude debs

Sixteen years ago I fancied myself a fearless street photographer barreling through the flux of human traffic in search of critical moments. I hovered around families, couples, and loners, public and private gatherings, legitimate and illegitimate commerce. In time, it dawned on me that I was more interested in what people were saying than in the way they looked. Even though I continued to snap the shutter, I stopped putting film in my camera. Eventually, I stopped carrying the camera altogether.

author's

The composition of each book in The Portrait Series is shaped by the composition of a life. The people who inspired these portraits have generously opened their lives, minds, and hearts to me over a period of at least seven years. My use of the first-person singular implies the autobiographical *I* of each subject. Their gospel, their memory, even their distortion is truth enough for me.

The monologues that make up this series are informed by the structure of supper talk, messages left on phone machines, ruminations of long walks, and reminiscences evoked by photo albums and rainy Sundays. In writing these books, I've taken liberties that a painter or photographer might take when a subject sits for a portrait. A turn of phrase, fragmentary memories, years of thought and conversation, are shaped into vignettes, short stories, confessions, diatribes, diagrams, and extended soliloquies. Many selections included in these books were developed out loud by way of readings and performance workshops.

THE PORTRAIT SERIES

note

a quartet of men

The first four books in **The Portrait Series** focus on men. Taken together, these books form a group portrait as reflective of the voices stirred within me as it is of the subjects. I offer these books to Claude, Brother Blue, Charlie, and Nicky D. as gifts in return for their trust and friendship. I also offer these books to you as an opportunity to visit with, listen to, and try to understand a life, a life's perspective, the lives of four eccentric, prismatic, and resilient men.

i give you complete
carte blanche

you can write about
the good

the bad
and the ugly

claude

Standing tall at barely five feet four, blue veins bulging from his neck, Claude Debs feels greatness boiling in his blood. When we first met fifteen years ago he was proud to tell me that his grandfather was the great American socialist Eugene Debs. Today, he couldn't care less. The past is the past and the past is dead.

A little over forty years ago in Paris, France, a boy is born with a shock of red hair and a curious look in his eyes. Soon afterwards both his parents die in a horrible accident. After a few years in an orphanage, a young couple take him away. They ask him to please consider them his parents. Growing up in different countries throughout the Middle East, Claude Debs is the son of the French ambassador. Inside the privileged walls of study rooms, library stacks, swimming pools, and shower stalls, an assortment of tutors, mentors, and teacher's aides take advantage of the fair-skinned, red-headed boy with unwanted fondling and genital probes. In time, an insatiable quest for knowledge, control, and sex forms a trilateral compass for his life. Endowed with a penetrating intellect and an unflappable will, Claude can and does transform himself in and out of a multitude of roles. As a semiprofessional student he's earned degrees in mathematics, chemistry, psychology, painting, graphic design, and medicine. Covering four continents in just over two decades, he has lived the life of a bohemian painter, entrepreneur, filmmaker, fashion photographer, undercover spy, doctor, philanthropist, homeless person, and successful businessman. Throughout his many incarnations, Claude has always been an inventor, a romantic, a schemer, and the hardest worker as well as the most sensuous and oversexed man I've ever met. Confrontation is his modus operandi. Although words and forceful argument are the only weapons I've ever seen him use, I picture Claude more at home in an era of chivalry, where men are prepared to duel to the death in order to preserve their honor. Underneath his defiant and assured persona, a daily battle rages between the challenges of the mind, the conscience of the soul, and the animal instincts of the glands. As an on-again off-again best friend throughout the years, Claude has been loyal, tender, possessive, generous, infuriating, and magical. This portrait lays bare the intimate reflections and fractious soliloquies of one side of a passionate, turbulent friendship, as seen by the other.

i don't give a **damn**
what anyone else
thinks about me

i **despise** the opinion
of other people
(you know that)

what i care about

is how **you** perceive me

how **you** perceive me

after fifteen years

that's

what i hold you

responsible for

you haven't known
brother blue
for fifteen years

i'm the only one
you've known

you haven't known
charlie for fifteen years

for fifteen years!

that's why you've got to

write it again and again

and again and again

till you get me in a nutshell

nothing less

do i expect of you

the ambassador's son

genesis

i
n

t
h
e

b
e
g
i
n
n
i
n
g

t
h
e
r
e

w
a
s

a

w
o
r
d

and the word was *a lie*

covering up another word

which was make-believe in the first place

they told me my real parents died when i was very young

i never met them / i don't remember if i did meet them or

if i didn't / i was very young when i was adopted / they

made up a birth date for me / it was to be my birthday

but i never fell for it / they told me they made it up!

i never fell for it!

never having a birthday has made my perspective on things

different / it's like playing baseball with no home plate

at best / a floating unreachable home plate in the midst of a

great fog / i don't dwell on the passing years / i don't keep

time / i couldn't tell you my age / it's better this way

j'ai l'âge de la pierre (i'm as old as stone)

it doesn't matter / i'll never really know / they made up some

date / they gave me a name / a couple of names

i never fell for it!

first encounter

unable to
breathe

my face shoved into
the darkness of
a hideous dank hell
gagging for air
i pray
i pray to be anywhere
other than inside
the horrible stench
that surrounds me
i try to pull away
not strong enough
i think
maybe i"m going to die

i'm six years old / i've had private tutors before / but this is my first year in an actual school (a catholic school in syria) i hate being cooped up inside a classroom all day / i look forward to eleven o'clock when you get to go outside and play in the school yard / you run around with other kids / make up different games / it's fun / then after playing outside you have to take a shower and get ready for lunch / the showers are okay / i never give it much thought really / until one day i'm taking a shower and this **big fat ugly woman** she isn't a teacher / she's like a guard / not a guard / you know / a uh / *an aide! a teacher's aide!* this very fat fat teacher's aide comes into the shower stall / out of nowhere turns off the water / she tells me to kneel down / she spreads her bulbous legs apart / lifts up her dress (i remember turning away / i didn't look because i was told that it was dirty / it was dirty to look at someone else's private parts / private parts are dirty) she takes hold of me by grabbing the back of my neck / covers my head with her dress / and presses my face between her thighs / i'm surrounded by darkness / complete darkness / i can't see a thing / i'm engulfed by hair and sweaty disgusting fatty flesh and a stinky stinky smell / i remember wondering *where's her pee pee? she doesn't have a pee pee it's just like a big cut or something* / i thought everybody had pee pees (i didn't even know the word for penis at the time) i have no idea what's going on / i try to pull my face up for air / but she's way too powerful / she tells me to kiss her **kiss me** she says **lick me / lick me like i'm a lollypop** / she forces my face deeper into her hole / then this huge huge woman sits down on the floor of the shower / hoists me up onto her lap and starts to play with my little pee pee / **she kisses it and touches it / she licks it** / afraid of suffocating under the weight of her mountainous body i start to panic / she turns me around and positions me this way and that (the whole thing is extremely awkward)

first encounter

she takes my limp little pee pee and tries to put it into her hole / it doesn't really go in (of course) so she grabs hold of it and rubs it against her / i'm in a state of shock and confusion and i'm scared / i know she can kill me very easily / all she has to do is sit on me / i think *maybe she just wants to be my friend* / *maybe she's playing a game with me* / *an adult game that she's letting me in on* / *maybe i did something wrong and she's punishing me* / whatever it is / i just wish it to be over *god* / *if there is a god and you're watching this*

stop it now

please

i don't want to die

i don't want to die

i don't know if i looked like i was about to cry or what but all of a sudden she takes me in her arms and hugs me

she hugs me! she kisses me / and then

she dresses me up / she helps me on with my pants / buttons up my shirt / ties my shoes / combs my hair / and tells me **you're such a good boy** / **such a nice boy** / then she takes me by the hand and brings me back to my classroom

the next morning i vomit / three / four times / i refuse to talk / i remain silent for two days / i don't eat / i don't feel like eating / i don't understand what's wrong with me / i just feel sick / i feel dirty and ugly / i know that i did *a bad thing* i know what she did to me was *a naughty thing* / and although i think it's probably my fault i know that she should know better / but i don't tell anyone (i never told anyone) why should i? at six years old i don't understand what it means to be violated / i don't understand the concept of humiliation adults hold supreme power and authority over any child even the son of an ambassador is constantly being handled pushed around / ignored / and told what to do / how can he distinguish a concept like child abuse or rape?

***

although this was the most violent / traumatic moment in my life (not to mention my first sexual encounter) it wasn't all that different from the way i normally was treated as a little kid / just more extreme / and being more extreme it made me feel all the more powerless / all the more susceptible to being pushed around / the real horror of the situation / the real horror was that this person / this lady / was around me all the time / i had to see her every day / as long as i was in that school i would see her / i would try my best to avoid her i would look away if i saw her coming / disappear inside my mind / i got to be very good at disappearing inside my mind but i knew / i always knew that as long as she was there / it could happen again at any moment / and you know / it never even occurred to me that she could have been doing the same thing to other kids / i thought that i was *chosen* / because i was the only white boy in the whole school / everybody else was dark / everybody else was an arab

now don't get all crazy on me here / it's no big deal it happened / and i got over it / that's all / what's the big deal? the truth is / it really hasn't affected me very much at all / hardly at all / except / except for the fact that still / to this day / vaginas are not one of my greatest interests i mean / it's / it's probably one of the reasons why i'm still turned off by a vagina / the smell / the taste / the whole thing is a turn off / i mean compared to assholes tits / legs / armpits / *anything but vaginas!*

brother felix

the brothers / oh man / the holy men of cloth / they're something else / this one brother / this teacher / his name was *brother felix* / he was in charge of the library

even at seven years old i cherished books / i loved to read that's why i was always **top of the class** / i'd go to the library after hours just to enjoy the books

brother felix may not have been very tall by adult standards but he towered over me with his bulging stomach and that nervous jerky twitch of his head that caused his chicken flesh neck to turn red around his collar / his priestly collar / i can see him now / brother felix / standing in front of a wall of dusty books / his arms and sweaty hands stretched out wide in a gesture of smug propriety and power / he's saying to me **all this is yours** / **what do you want?**

normally / it would've been impossible to have more than one book out at a time / but brother felix would let me have four five books all at once! i'd say *well* / *i'd like to have this book and this book and these two books* / and sure enough there they were / mine to take

but then / he would **grab me** from behind while i was looking at a book / he would **touch me** / he **would touch my ass** / he would **touch me all around** / at the same time he would play with himself / rubbing his pee pee he would **masturbate** behind me he did this a lot at first i was shocked

after a while i became disgusted

eventually i played along with it / because i was very much
interested in the books / with brother felix on my side i had
access to the whole library / all i had to do was let him touch
me a little and any book i wanted i could have

don't get me wrong

i hated him!
i hated this man
to think of him makes me
nauseous
makes me mad
i'm very mad!

not because he abused me / i'm mad at the fact that he used
my other interests / all the other people who abused me
they didn't use my other interests / they just used my body
and that's okay / i can accept that / but brother felix used
my other interests / my interest in reading / he took
advantage of that / and that is sort of rotten / but i'm not
going to make a big fuss about it / tell you the truth
i used him as much as he used me / for instance / if i
wanted to take out a reference book / like an atlas or an
encyclopedia (which nobody was supposed to take out of the
library) i'd please him by putting on shorts (short shorts)

listen / i knew he was a **sick man** / i knew that what he
did to me was dirty / but i got what i wanted too / he had the
key to the library / he possessed the key to knowledge / all
adults manipulate children in one way or another / order
them around / shove them this way and that / at least with
brother felix there was a payoff / i paid with my ass
i got knowledge in return

brother felix

look / even back then i knew how extremely hypocritical it was for a priest to do something like that / you know / after asking us to go to communion and become devout christians and then to do something like that! but what moved me about the man was / well / one day / in front of the whole class brother felix was giving a lecture on christ's moment of temptation / he was saying things like **there comes a time when those of the holiest of intentions** / *even the divine jesus christ himself* / **become seduced by the lure of the flesh** / then he said *i myself have been tempted by devilish* / *earthly thoughts* / **even i a man of the cloth** / **a teacher of young children** / **even i have sinned even i**

have sinned!

he went on and on in a convoluted neurotic way / alluding to a secret personal crisis / standing there underneath the french and lebanese flags / in front of my whole class of seven-year-old children / he started to cry / mumbling something about **what is temptation? where does it come from? how can we find the strength to resist its grip?** then he looked directly into my eyes and said **sometimes** / **sometimes** / **i get so tempted sometimes** / **so tempted** / **so tempted**

he was sobbing / asking for forgiveness / i felt certain that i was the only one who knew what he was talking about brother felix gave me a perspective on the fragility of man

as young as i was i could see a man tormented by his desires

i took pity on his struggle for redemption / i saw his weakness

his shame / he became so small in my eyes / when you're a

kid you see your teacher as a huge / a powerful giant / and i

was no exception / i looked up to my teachers / but after i saw

this grown man / *this priest* / shrink in front of my eyes

after seeing him become so small / so vulnerable / it helped

me feel not so bad about myself / it helped me to see that i

was as good if not better than anybody else / even

grown-ups / even my teacher / i made

peace with myself / with my own condition / kids are full of

temptations / chocolates and candies / stealing little things

this and that / to know that adults could actually be weak

elevated my own self-worth / parents / teachers / priests

they're like omnipotent / unbeatable little gods / to a child

and to see a god fall i think matured me at a very early age

i made peace with what it meant to be alive / i made peace

with what it meant to be a little boy / and what

it would mean to become a man

sitting in my chair / looking at brother felix / i made peace

with my environment / perhaps for the first time in my

young life / i saw things as they really are / for the first time

i accepted the cruel hypocrisy and injustice of a world

i never asked to be a part of

fleur de lune

if an out-of-town guest comes to visit for the first time chances are you're going to take them around to see the very best sights you can think of / it's only natural to want to make a strong impression on someone who comes from far away / if you're a dignitary it's your job to show foreign dignitaries the most magnificent spectacles your country has to offer / as the son of an ambassador i was carted around to so many incredible places i practically built up an immunity to being impressed / by the time i was seven years old i'd been to so many mosques / palaces / pyramids / shrines / caves and mountaintops / the idea of going to marrakesh to see the *fleur de lune* meant virtually nothing to me

it was an all male expedition for some reason / the ambassador from marrakesh and some of his men / my father with a few of his men and i paddled up a north african river in a sweltering heat / our heads wrapped tight in handkerchiefs soaking up pools of sweat / shielding us from an unrelenting sun / it must have been at least one hundred and ten degrees in the shade / damn! it was hot! every hour or so we'd stop to rest under the shade of the occasional bamboo tree that spotted the riverbank / being a restless little kid i'd wander off to explore the arid desert that lay just beyond the edge of the river / but there was nothing to see / there was nothing but endless stretches of barren sand / with no place else to rest my eyes i looked down at my feet only to discover a shimmering piece of topaz (which i knew to be a precious stone) i couldn't believe i'd found a valuable gem like that in the middle of nowhere / at every stop along the way i dug up more of these precious stones until my pockets were bursting with rocks / after about a half day's journey canoeing up

the river / one of the marrakeshi men said to my father

this is it / *we're here!* i looked around to see

what he was talking about / there was nothing to see but

desert / we carried our gear for a few miles further inland

until we came to a spot with millions of dark colorless stems

sticking up out of the vast expanse of sand / i couldn't

understand what all the fuss was about / of all the

places i'd been dragged to / this was by far

the biggest disappointment

while the men worked on erecting a big square tent

i set out in search of more topaz / after finding a few more

stones i pulled my father aside to show him my secret treasure

i figured the money we could get for the topaz would be our

ticket out of the middle east / my father wouldn't have to kiss

up to all these people anymore / *look at all of this topaz*

i found / *we're rich! we're rich!* my father's jaw dropped as

he looked at the handful of jewels **oh my god claude!**

i was so proud / he called over to one of the marrakeshi men

come look at this / the man picked up one of the

stones and burst out laughing / he said something to my

father in a dialect i didn't understand / then walked away

laughing hysterically / i asked my father what was so funny

it's not really topaz my father said regretfully / **it's a rock**

found in great abundance around here / **they call it**

fool's topaz / **they call it** ***the precious stone of fools***

i was doubly disappointed / not only had i worked so hard

digging up stones that turned out to be completely worthless

i was surrounded by grown-ups / stuck in the middle

of a major nonwonder of the world

when night came (around six or seven) the sun set / the sky

darkened / and then underneath the glow of a full moon the

whole desert opened up into a vast field of huge white flowers

i couldn't believe my eyes!

it was such a glorious sight / without thinking i ran from the tent headlong into the blanket of white flowers / each flower was so gigantic my seven-year-old hand couldn't even reach the tips of the opened petals / i jumped for joy inside that fragrant field of white / then i walked back to the tent and stood there with the other men / flabbergasted at the endless web of flowers stretching for miles and miles before our eyes

the marrakeshi men prepared a party for us that night / they grilled a mutton / mixed up a special drink / picked some of the flowers to put in a vase / set the table / and then suddenly a wind came and tipped everything over into the sand / the table / the mutton / the grill / and all the dishes / everything was ruined! the hosts were so upset / here they wanted to make a big show for my father and *voompf* / i thought it was funny / i didn't care / the flowers were such a delicious sight / i didn't care whether we ate or not

after about two hours or so the flowers started to turn back down in the direction of the earth / the stems weakened and with some help from the blowing wind the flowers slowly closed their petals / the next day when we woke up all the flowers were completely closed / i asked my father if we could stay another night to see the flowers open up again / this man they called my father (whoever he was) lifted me onto his lap and told me that the *fleur de lune* (the moon flower) wouldn't open for another year / **only once a year does the *fleur de lune* open its petals to the light of the full moon** / then he proceeded to give me my vocabulary word for the day / i have to give him credit for that / this man / this so-called father of mine never read me bedtime stories / but almost every night before i went to sleep he would put me on his knees and teach me a word or expression that had something to do with an experience i had earlier in the day / there in the middle of that north african desert / early that morning my father taught me a vocabulary word that i'd never ever forget / he looked at me and said **well claude** / **today you learned about** *éphémère* / *éphémère* **is a word that means** *something that doesn't last for very long* / then he looked out into the desolate field of bare stems and said **happiness is** *éphémère* / **joy is** *éphémère* / **life** he said **is full of experiences** / **and many of them are cruel or unjust or simply don't make any sense at all** / **but the happiest experiences are usually** *éphémère* / **the most beautiful things in life don't last** / **in fact they're very short-lived** / **so whenever you come across a good thing whenever you encounter a happy or beautiful experience you must enjoy it** / **you must savor every morsel of it because if it is good** / **it cannot last for very long**

that was the lesson i got from my father as a little boy from the experience of the moon flower / a lesson that has stuck with me ever since

everywhere i turned

my father was continually being reassigned as the french

ambassador to different countries within the middle east

as soon as i got used to one place i had to move to another

nothing was routine / depending on the situation i would go

from being in secular schools to catholic schools to having

private tutors / in every case *there was always abuse*

i was this red-haired / fair-skinned boy from france in the

midst of all these dark brown people / i clearly stood out

as being different / which both made it hard for me

to fit in and attracted people to me

in syria

my arabic professor (a private tutor) used to undo his zipper
take out his big fat cock all the way out
and then he'd pull down my pants
and try to penetrate me from
behind / he'd put his finger in my ass
while he was teaching me how to
conjugate arabic verbs / he would
teach me while my hand was on his
penis / masturbating him / the funny thing
was / he would do this in my father's study room while my
father was right upstairs / i hated him! i hated him
like i hated them all / i knew that he was doing *naughty things*
to me / i knew because he wouldn't do it in front of my
parents / nobody did it in front of my parents

in lebanon

the british embassy owned this big beautiful pool / the water was a calm aqua blue and very warm / i loved to float on my back and disappear into another world / i'd look up at the sky letting in precisely the right amount of light needed to create constellations of microscopic circular rainbows across the surface of my eyes / and then **out of nowhere** this guy (an arab who worked for the embassy) would **sneak behind me in the pool** he'd always do this / **he'd sneak behind me and then he'd stick his pudgy disgusting finger way up my ass**

right there in the pool!

in egypt

try to understand that when you're in another country as a little kid / you always want to be accepted / you want to be accepted by the teacher / you want approval from the figures of authority / but you also want the approval of kids your own age / i wanted to be accepted by my own age group too / it's only natural to want to be liked / to be a part of your peer group / i was eight and nine years old when we were in egypt i had only one real friend: rafaic / he would beg me (we'd be studying together) and he would **beg me** / he'd say **okay** / **i'll study with you** / **if you let me** / i'd say *no* / *we won't study then!* so he'd just sit there next to me sulking / then he'd say **please . . . please** / i'd be wearing shorts (like all kids do) but rafaic took advantage / he would pinch me inside my shorts / he'd tease me and then he'd beg me **please please please please** / eventually i let him the first time he just kissed my penis / he gave it the tiniest

everywhere i turned

little peck / the next time he took hold of it and kissed it

with a fierce passion / after a while he just sucked on it

like it was a popsicle

i just couldn't be
anywhere or do
anything without
having somebody
come and stick
something up my ass
and if it wasn't that
then it was my penis
they were after / it was
terrible / it seemed so
stupid to me / so
annoying

but rafaic was my favorite friend / he was very very sensitive

so i let him do it / in return i got his friendship

in saudi arabia

i never told anyone about any of these incidents / not about

brother felix / or the fat lady in the shower / the tutors

i never told anybody about any of it / this is the first time

i've ever talked about these . . . these . . . episodes to anyone

except once / only once did i ever snitch:

it was on the vegetable man

i was very close to the chef (the head chef) he taught me his culinary secrets / i was his helper / his little elf / i loved him / i'd help him by chopping vegetables / washing fish and meat / stirring stews and sauces / cleaning up / any little thing i could do for him / he'd often send me to the market to pick up whatever extra ingredients he needed / including vegetables / i felt honored that he trusted me to go alone to the market / the only problem was / whenever i would buy vegetables from the vegetable man he would touch me / he'd stick his hand down my pants and grab at me / i hated this filthy man and his vegetables!

but i adored the chef and wouldn't do anything to disobey him / so finally one day i told my father *i don't like to go to the market* / *i don't want to go there again* / he asked me **why?** i said *well* / *the man* / *the vegetable man touches me when i go there* / *he touches me here* / *and here* / *and here* / *he tries to stick his finger up my tushy* / *he grabs me* / my father looked straight at me and said **why do you let him? don't let him get away with that** / **the next time he does this to you throw all his vegetables** / **take the whole big thing** / **his whole stand** / **and throw it on the ground** / **then tell the man: don't you ever do that to me again!** / **show him he can't push you around like that anymore**

my father didn't call the police / he didn't go himself and fight the guy / he didn't try to run the vegetable man out of business or use his power to publicly denounce or humiliate him / he didn't get hysterical / he didn't try to reassure or comfort me he didn't even tell my mother / he didn't make a big scene at all / i think if he had done these things / then i would have clearly known that this was a *really bad thing* for someone to do / that all the people who did these things to me were bad and that something *really awful* / *really terribly damaging* had happened to me / but no / he didn't react that way at all

everywhere i turned

at the time i felt betrayed by my father's reaction / i wanted

him to go and smash the guy's face in / finish him off / i

wanted him to ask me if anyone else ever touched me like that

i wanted him to protect me / i wanted him to be furious

i wanted him to be my personal hero / but he was just a wet

noodle / to me he was less than a real man / i wanted him to

be a man of action / but he was all talk / always talk (in fact

when i left my parents at age thirteen / i told my father that

he was always talk and no action) as a politician his whole

career was talking / he never really actually helped anyone

it's only now / in retrospect / it's only now that i'm thankful

that my father didn't make a big hoopla / a big

deal / a big american deal out of the

whole thing / with policemen and lawyers and

therapists and support groups and newspapers and filling out

reports and sobbing relatives YOU POOR THING / YOU

POOR THING / you know how they go on and on in this

country about being a victim / all the mass hysteria / and the

t.v. talk shows / the docudramas on pedophilia / articles in

pop psychology magazines / twelve-step programs and

hundreds and hundreds of books / americans professionalize

self-pity! steel mills and auto plants are closing down all over

the country / manufacturers can't compete with foreign

markets / but the self-pity industry is booming in this country

booming! all over the world women and

children are raped every day of the week / it's a terrible thing

but they get over it / except in america

people turn self-pity into an art / YOU POOR THING

YOU POOR THING / so you feel justified in whining and

whimpering your whole life / you think you require / you

need to be handled with kid gloves / for fifty / sixty / seventy

years you think of yourself as damaged goods / i'm glad i

didn't have to put up with any of that . . . that stigma of being

violated / being abused / being *homosexualized* / i'm really

thankful i wasn't put through all that / because the lack of it the lack of any commotion meant that sex wasn't such a

big deal / it wasn't such a *naughty thing* / all these parts

these appendages and crevices / they weren't dirty / they were

meant to be touched / of course my father wasn't clever

enough to know that he was doing the right thing / but in a

strange way his reaction conveyed just enough for me to know

that grown-ups shouldn't ever touch the private parts of little

kids / but that if it did happen / it wasn't the worst thing that

could happen to a child / it wasn't such a horrendous horrible

crime / and that if it happens to you / and you really

don't like it / at a certain point you can just say

don't you ever do that to me again!

to be abused as a child / it's a bad thing / maybe even terrible

but you just get over it / that's all

just get over it!

the leader of the pack

although i grew up in a foreign land / the only white kid
around / in time i was always accepted by the other children
because i was the smartest / wherever we went i became

the leader of the pack

no matter where we were / the other kids wanted me on
their team / if we were playing war out on the street or on the
grounds of the embassy / my team would always win because
of my ingenious strategies and sense of weapon design / i was
a specialist in warfare because the napoleonic wars were part
of my studies / i was fascinated with artillery / particularly
armaments / how could the local arab kids compete with a
training like mine? while they were limited to throwing
stones with their hands / i constructed guns with
bayonets / i concocted a gun device i called

The **BOOM BOOM**™

i made it by attaching three braided bands of this very heavy
elastic to a piece of flat board (they used the elastic in the
embassy for belts inside heater engines and things like that)
i'd take balloons filled with water and then fire them from my
BOOM BOOM™ machine into the enemy / they'd go
much farther than any balloon you could throw by hand
much farther! sometimes i would fill the balloons with oil
oil balloons were very very popular / because a kid who gets a
balloon with oil flopped on his head has to get out of the war
he has to go home and wash up / he's finished! he's a dead
man / i got the oil from the chef at the embassy / he didn't
exactly know what i was using it for / he probably thought
i was just making little experiments / he had no idea
i was using the oil in my secret life as a warrior

another invention of mine was

The DUST MAKER ™

everywhere you go in the arab world you see white paint

that they make from a kind of a white chalk mixed with water

so what i would do / i'd dry this white chalk and pulverize it

i'd have one group of kids pounding the chalk with rocks to

get it to just the right consistency / while another group of

kids operated the electric fans / we'd plug the fans into outlets

outside the embassy with long extension cords / and then

we'd just blow this white powder into the faces

of the approaching enemy

if we were conducting warfare away from the embassy

away from any power supply / instead of electric fans i'd have

a group of kids fan the powder with pieces of board / really

really fast / you'd be surprised how effective the hand-fanning

technique was in the middle of a big battle / let me tell you

when that powder got on the kids who were already hit with

oil balloons / it stuck to their clothes / their skin / it was

a fantastic combination! sure / sometimes

the wind would blow the powder back on us / it happened

but that was okay / when you're the leader of the pack / the

commander and chief / you have to be prepared to take risks

and accept the casualties / you rise to the top of the fray

you play the edge / you run the risk of falling off

two early encounters

1

i'm running after this girl
(the daughter of another ambassador in the neighborhood)
she's a year younger than me / maybe she's five or six years old
we're playing some game / something like tag / i go to tag
her and i think by accident my hand lands in her armpit / i
discover i get some kind of a kick out of running after her and
putting my finger under her armpit / every time i do it we
just kind of look at each other / then continue to play

later in the evening / i visualize the image of chasing her

i picture my fingers in her armpit

and i / well / it's not that i touch my penis with my hand
i mean at six years old i didn't do that (consciously) what i did
do though / i remember because i continued to do this for a
long time / i lay down on my bed / flat on my stomach
and then i raised my body away from the mattress so that my
genitals were lightly / very lightly touching the bed / creating
just a little bit of friction / ever so slightly / up then down
back and forth / ever so slightly

i didn't understand the relationship between her armpit
and my genitals / i mean / i knew *something* was happening
i think it was my very first realization that to touch another
human being was a source of pleasure / so i developed
strategies and invented games where i would run after this girl
and the ultimate goal was to end up with my hand
under her armpit / i must've thought

there is something going on here

i constructed the games so that no matter how many other kids were playing / she would always be my adversary / there was a great deal of pleasure in the chase / culminating in a hand in an armpit / i never could understand why / i tried the same thing with her brother but it didn't work! i think if her brother did respond to this / if it did work with him / if he giggled in the same way or dared me never to do it again / i'd probably have become homosexual or at least i'd be bisexual this was such an important moment in my development!

2

about a year later i experienced a similar stimulation / we were living in lebanon at the time / and i was playing with this girl / a different girl / her name was hoda / i was sort of attracted to her i guess / maybe we were both eight / well she slapped me so hard during a game / she was supposed to *catch me* / but she *slapped me* so hard on my back that it hurt / it really hurt me / but it was also extremely exciting being hit by this girl and really being hurt by her / extremely exciting!

from that moment on / i associated that kind of touch with the ultimate contact i could have with a woman / and i suppose that vicious sado-masochistic sort of pleasure has stuck with me ever since

goddess

the very idea of being with a woman at the age of ten or eleven

a

WOMAN

to have a woman next to me was such a totally big

completely staggering concept / that it . . . it . . . it . . .

it left my brain breathless / i couldn't possibly come close to

imagining the pleasure one could have by being with a woman

not just a girl but a **woman** / an older woman

my curiosity was insatiable!

i decided i couldn't wait five or ten years / i had to experience

that feeling for myself right away / i snuck some sheets and a

blanket out of the linen closet / found a pair of my father's old pajamas from the bureau in my parents' bedroom / returned

to my room (in the embassy) locked the door behind me

stuffed the linens into the pajama bottoms and rolled them

into the shape of two legs culminating in the curve of an ass

then i took the blanket and used it for the torso and the arms

i stole one of the maid's whatchamacallits / uh / *hairdos*

you know / not hairdos / uh / wigs! i took one of her

wigs and attached it to the top of a pillow head / then i filled

up two balloons with water to just the right shape / warm

water / they were the breasts / in the end i constructed

a full-sized amorphous female body

i kept her (it) hidden in a secret place / then late at night i'd

close my door and sneak it into bed with me / once under the

covers i'd become submerged by this feeling / i was totally

submerged / i would rub myself / i would masturbate / it

was a feeling of too much overwhelming passion

very early on i discovered that i only had two hands / i

couldn't imagine how / how a real / how with a real

woman / how could i ever . . . i mean now i understand

more / because i had one hand on my penis and i only had

one hand left to enjoy two tits / one ass / two legs / and the

neck and everything / you see / i could only concentrate on

one part of the body at a time / i'd fixate on the feeling of one

of the balloon tits or the crotch or the neck / whatever part it

was / it was enough for me to reach that extreme feeling

of pleasure / i thought to myself *my god!*

it must be impossible / a woman is

too much / you have so many places

you can't concentrate!

i mean / even with my make-believe woman there

were so many surfaces to touch / so many things to enjoy

i remember the first actual woman / the first real woman that

i was with / she was naked in front of me / it took me

goddess

ten minutes just looking at her / thinking

**my goodness / it's right there in
front of me / all the parts
the real thing!**

the relationship with my make-believe pajama goddess

continued for quite some time / until one night / my mother

came into my room and saw this . . .

this . . .

this . . .

this . . .

THING

lying next to me
with its big balloon tits
and rolled-up linen ass

it was traumatic (for both of us)

she gasped
what is that?

i said *no / this is uh / no / it's just / i'm uh / you know / i'm*

just making a friend / making a play or something

i don't know what excuse i gave

after a while / i began to notice that these . . . these things
these activities / these inventions and games that felt so good
to me / so incredibly good and vital were considered by adults
to be very *naughty* / shameful / and bad for you / and i
realized that i would either have to abandon this area
of experimentation or master the skills of
concealment and deceit

fertile earth

we

were

traveling

up

the

nile

on

our

way

to visit

some very important person in northern sudan

my father's whole entourage came with us on this trip

(an economics person / two consuls / a protocol guy / a cook

their wives and children) one day i found this beautiful bird

that got caught in a net / when my father saw me playing with

the bird / he snapped **it's not your bird**

put it back / put it back!

later that night we camped in a forest near the river

i was so upset about the bird and my father's reaction to

the bird / i just couldn't sleep / i crept outside our tent and

found a spot on a rock with a view of the nile to the east and

the woods behind me to the west / somehow i managed to fall

asleep right on the rock / i woke up just before dawn to the

sound of rustling in the bush / being right by the river the

terrain was so lush i couldn't see through the thick foliage

i thought maybe the noises were coming from some kind

of large animal / i tiptoed through the woods to see what

it could be / *maybe it was a buffalo or a herd of wildebeests!*

to my surprise i discovered a whole group of (maybe a dozen

or so) very thin / very tall / very naked men from this one tribe / normally the men from this tribe wore pants and shirts but for some reason they were only wearing loincloths and carrying tall walking sticks / i had a couple of hours before breakfast so i followed behind them / i was a kid! and like all kids i loved adventure / i loved mysteries / but after about an hour (getting deeper and deeper into the jungle) i started to get scared / i wasn't scared of the men from the tribe / after all i was a white guy / i was the son of a white man / they would never lift a finger to me / it was the wild animals i was scared of / at one point i got completely lost / i lost track of the men / i lost my sense of direction / i was lost altogether / so i climbed up this huge rock to see if i could find my way / and to my amazement i saw one of the men

masturbating onto the skull of a cow skeleton

i knew what he was doing because at twelve years old (as you know by now) i had been masturbating for a couple of years myself / i looked for the rest of the men in his tribe *where were they?* i walked along an embankment of rocks until i saw another man masturbating into a little brook / i saw two other men doing it onto the trunks of trees / the remaining eight or nine men congregated up on a dirt hill then separated / once they found their own little patch of territory / each man made a hole straight down

into the ground with his walking stick

then took off his loincloth

lay down flat on his stomach

inserted his penis

into

the

hole

beneath

him

and started humping the earth

they thrust their hip

they grunted howle

they fucked the grou

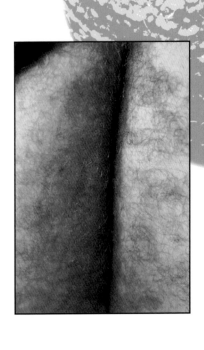

nto the dirt

i couldn't believe what i was watching / i knew that men and

nd groaned

women did this together / but i never heard of men doing it

d beneath them!

with the earth / i was flabbergasted! i'll never forget the

choreography of all those naked butts going up and down

up and down / up and down / up and down

---

as usual / i never told my parents what i saw / i never asked

them to explain it to me / i felt worlds apart from them / i

always did / i never shared my adventures / my thoughts

with anybody / so i really had no idea what it was that i saw

until many years later i read in a book that the men of this

one tribe (and several other tribes in africa / in sudan) have

a custom / once a year / of going out into the land and

impregnating the ground as well as the water / the trees

and the bones of dead animals / in order to ensure that the

earth will be fertile and rich / so that come next season

they'll have plenty of animals to hunt

first flight

for two years i was trying and trying / actually i was doing it

i was masturbating for two years / i was trying

actually i was doing it / i was trying and trying / i was

masturbating without ejaculating / i was trying and

trying / actually i was doing it / reaching orgasm

at ten years old / i was reaching orgasm

without ejaculating

i was doing it / i was doing it / i was

trying / i was trying and trying

actually i was doing it / i was

masturbating / i was reaching

orgasm without ejaculating

without ejaculating

anything for almost a year

and then when i turned eleven / i kept

trying / i just kept trying and trying

and trying / reaching / trying

reaching / actually i was doing it

without ejac . . . without

ejaculating anything

for almost a year

trying / reaching / i was trying / i was

reaching / because i knew / i knew

what was supposed to happen

so i just kept trying

and then when i turned twelve years old / i tried even harder

i was actually doing it without / you know / without

ejaculating / i tried so hard / so hard / believe me

i tried every day / i would do it / two / three / four

times a day / i tried so hard / so hard

and then one day i was doing it / i was trying / like i was

always trying / trying

trying / reaching

trying / and i remember

my shock / my absolute

shock / i was doing it / like i

was always doing it / i was trying

reaching / reaching / trying / and i

remember my shock / my absolute

shock / when that one day / i was doing it

i was doing it / i was doing it / i was trying and trying and

trying and trying / and something

something started happening that

was different / it felt different

somehow / something / i mean i

was doing it like i was always doing it

i was trying like i always was trying

trying trying trying trying trying

trying trying trying trying / reaching

reaching reaching / trying / reaching

and my shock / my shock

my absolute shock / when

that one day i was doing it

and all of a sudden

it

just

shot

out

of

me

like

a

rocket

bedroom

it didn't matter what country we were in / my home was
always the embassy / *the french embassy* / and the suite of the
ambassador was always outrageously spacious and extravagant
my room was always very large / very plush / very expensive
i had the best of everything material / i always had at least
two of everything / i had two bathrooms all for myself
and there'd always be two very large beds in my bedroom
wherever we were / because most of the other ambassadors
had at least two children / and for most of my childhood
career i was the only kid in my family

i was continually made aware of the fact that i was alone

every
night
i'd
get
into
my
bed

and
the
other
one
would
always
be
empty

six years after i was adopted by my "parents" / my mother
finally gave birth to a child of her own / of my parents' own
making / a son / my so-called half-brother *andré* / he was the
jewel in their crown / *andré* / they didn't want him to grow
up in the middle east / that was okay for me / but andré

deserved to have a european environment for his formative years / so they sent him to live with an aunt and a nanny in paris / it wasn't until he was five years old that he came to live with us in alexandria / i was already eleven by then / i left my family when i was thirteen / so i only really knew this other boy for two years / maybe a little less / and / well / in the beginning i looked forward to having a brother / i was always alone / so i thought it would be fun to have a little playmate for a change / but it wasn't fun at all / he turned out to be a big bore / the kid was just too young for me / at eleven years old i had already seen the world / all of a sudden i was forced to baby-sit this five-year-old / well-behaved / sheltered little pip-squeak / here i was / a sophisticated / mature / tough kid on the verge of becoming a man / i didn't want to have this limp dishrag hanging around me all the time / as soon as he entered the picture everything changed / nothing was like it was before i went from being the only child to just one of the kids my bedroom became *our* bedroom

every
night
i'd
get
into
my
bed

and
the
other
one
was
no
longer
empty

i'd look across the room at andré's innocent little sleeping face and feel even more aware of the fact that i was alone i had no choice but to sleep next to this boy they called my brother / i had no choice but to sleep next to someone who

bedroom

could never really understand me / before andré i was alone
after andré i was lonely / i had no excuse to feel lonely / i was
inescapably **not alone** / at eleven years old i realized
that this feeling of loneliness was an inevitable condition of life
i remember thinking *no matter how many people you surround*
yourself with / *you're alone* / *you're born alone* / *you live alone*
no matter what you do / *what job you have* / *no matter how*
famous you become / *whether you're an ambassador or a war*
hero or the greatest genius that ever lived / *no matter if you have*
a large family / *a small family* / *no matter how many so-called*
brothers and parents and aunts and uncles / *no matter how*
much you try to fill your life up with fancy things / *big houses*
and lots of fancy friends and jewelry and precious objects / *you*
are alone / *you can't escape it* / *you sleep alone (even in the*
company of others) your dreams take place inside your own
private skull / *alone* / *you talk to yourself all day* / *thinking*
alone / *within the walls of your own mind* / *all day* / *alone*
all night / *all of your life* / *no matter where you are*
or who you're with / *you're always alone inside*

i remember lying there across from andré thinking
one day i will be married and i'll be very lonely with my wife
even if she loves me and i love her / *nobody* / *nobody can ever*
really fully know another person / *nobody can ever really fully be*
with another person / *you can't get inside their brain with them*
maybe you can touch another person / *brush up against them*
but you can't get inside their skin with them / and then / i
remember actually thinking *one day i will be very very sick*
i'll be dying actually / *and with or without a wife or a friend*
or even a brother by my deathbed / *i will finally die* / *just like*
i came into this world alone / *all alone and of little consequence*
and then once dead i will (in a short time) most likely be
forgotten / *wiped out forever and ever and ever and ever and*
ever and ever / *dead! lying in a casket* / *or . . . or . . . or reduced*
to a clump of ashes in an urn left on a mantelpiece somewhere

forgotten | nobody in there but me | not even me!

nothing but bones and ashes | no wife or brother or god in there

nothing even gone off to heaven (as young as i was i had already

completely rejected my religious studies) *no soul | no hell*

no purgatory | no angels | nothing (to expect) *but death*

that's all | empty | meaningless | everlasting death

many years later | i woke up in a cold sweat in the middle

of the night | calling out to my (first) wife

marizette

marizette

marizette

i'm lonely

i feel terribly lonely

can you understand that?

she looked at me and said

no

then went back to sleep

i've since grown to accept the separateness of existence | in

fact i cherish my aloneness | i've cut off my family | i don't

collect friends or material possessions | i never stay long

enough to call any place a home | and with no attachments

on my body or in my heart | i remain (to the best of my

knowledge) the happiest man alive

the arabian delicacy

i didn't know where we were

it's hard to know exactly where you are
when you're twelve years old
and in the middle of a vast desert

all i knew was that we were
. . . *somewhere*

on a long journey between saudi arabia and yemen

and that we were staying the night at a royal compound as the

guests of a sheik and his entourage / my father had some kind

of business to do with the sheik / some kind of *deal* to

make with him / and that meant that i was to be

on my best behavior

stuck in the middle of nowhere / with no other children to

play with / i wandered around the compound until (to my

complete delight) i discovered three monkeys tied to a pole

behind one of the tents / **real monkeys!** they

seemed to be a family / two parents and an adorable little

baby / i never actually saw a monkey that was a pet before

i'd seen monkeys in zoos / i sort of remembered seeing wild

monkeys in india when i was just two or three years old / but

i never actually got to play with a real monkey / with a pet

monkey / i must've spent at least an hour playing with them

before i was called for dinner / i gave them names / the

mother was *cora* / the father *mongo* / and the little one

was *zuzu* / he was so cute / he was the most precious

adorable / affectionate little monkey you could imagine

i spoke with zuzu in his own language

dinner

was

served

on

a

long

wooden

table

inside a tent / which was like so many other tents inhabited

by so many other kings and shahs and sheiks and emirs and the

whole assortment of important people i had already eaten with

in the arab world / we sat in the customary way / on the

the arabian delicacy

matted floor / legs folded beneath the table / a towering giant

of a man in a long green robe stood above me

pouring tea out of a kettle

the tea streamed down through the air like a waterfall into the center of

my tiny tea cup

i was amazed that such casual / almost absent-minded

gracefulness could result in such precise aim / i felt clumsy

and uncomfortable in my starched shirt and tight little tie

why could these people walk around in their loose flowing

bathrobes and i had to dress up all the time

like i was a penguin at a funeral?

the first few courses were the usual fare: eggplant salad

roasted squab / moussaka / couscous / goat's milk / things

that i hated at that age / i hated eating squab / i didn't like

the idea of eating pigeon / *it was gross* / also / in the middle

east they always serve food on this big platter / this big dish in

the center of the table / you just grab what you want with

your hands / i never got used to that custom / everybody's

dirty hands grabbing at food / strangers putting their

grubby fingers into everything / yuk!

halfway through dinner the sheik announced that we were all

in for **a very very special treat** / he said that since my father was including him and his people in some **new and promising business venture** / and because it was **such an honor to have the privilege** of my father's company and the company of **his wonderful family and staff** he was going to **treat us all to the ultimate** / **the absolute number one delicacy** of his people

there was a feeling of something special about to happen i figured they were probably going to bring out this outrageous dessert / like a humongous chocolate ice cream cake with pounds of whipped cream cherries / strawberries / and hot fudge

the servants passed out these wooden hammers / they were like little bats with one sharp edge / i took hold of mine like it was a toy and started jabbing it into the air / fighting off an imaginary enemy (the way kids do) i remember everybody laughing / they thought i was being so cute / i hated that! i hated being the cute little kid / all i wanted was to have some fun / a little fun for a change / so there i was playing with my neat little hammer / my new toy / when one of the sheik's servants came out carrying zuzu / the little baby monkey he was holding him in his arms / i called out

ZUZU ZUZU!

i was so happy / i went crazy over it / the servant showed off the little monkey to my father / as though zuzu was a bottle of vintage wine / seeking his approval / my father seemed quite pleased / he nodded / i figured he loved zuzu too / who wouldn't love this beautiful little monkey? / *oohs* and *ahhs* circulated around the table / i reached out to pet the monkey

zuzuzuzuzuzuzuzuz

my mother stopped me *be careful! he'll scratch you*

the arabian delicacy

i started making monkey sounds / talking with zuzu

after showing off zuzu to all the guests / the sheik's servant took him underneath the table / put his head up through a hole in the center of the table / tightened some screws into something like a vise / so that zuzu's head was secured above the table / with the rest of his body below / i thought that we were all going to play a game / some kind of a game / *feed the monkey* or something like that / then the sheik asked my father if he would **do us all the honor of having the first crack** / so my father (being the perfect diplomat that he was) sort of half smiled / picked up the little hammer took a little breath and knocked the skull of the monkey he gave it one swift knock / zuzu let out a hair-raising shriek that pierced the walls of the tent and shot out into the desert

the look on zuzu's face
was sheer terror / he understood what
was going on more than i did / he was trapped
he was completely trapped / he looked at me with
pleading eyes / my heart lurched straight up into my throat
pounding a thousand beats a second / i was shocked / i was
furious with my father for doing such a thing / i wanted
to scream out / i wanted to scream and yell / but i was too
well trained / i knew that i was in no position to do anything
about it / as a form of protocol i knew that i could never
question what my father did / and that i was never ever to

the arabian delicacy

question the customs of another race of people / no matter
how strange or revolting they may seem to me

a
volcano
was
erupting
inside
my
body

and yet / i just sat there / i sat there and watched as everybody
took their little hammers one at a time and crashed them down
into zuzu's howling / screeching / screaming / bloody head
the arab men just kept hitting the poor little monkey over and
over again / the sheik came over to my mother **huh huh**
he ha / he was laughing real hard **huh huh he**
ha haaa huh huh / he was enjoying himself so
much / he was so proud / so proud of having orchestrated a
masterful conquest over this defenseless little primate / he
gestured for my mother to give it a shot / i looked up at her
trying to imagine what she would do to get out of it / but
to my complete surprise and horror / she picked up her little
hammer and with a faint gesture from the wrist / she made
a little tap that met with zuzu's head

the sheik seemed disappointed that all of this was taking so
long / by this point zuzu was no longer struggling / no longer
fighting for his life / resigned now to defeat / all he
could do was weep and gasp for air

the sheik gestured towards me with his droopy eyes
go on / go on
give it a good

i was paralyzed / i didn't even pretend to lift a finger / then all
of a sudden / the sheik took his hammer / and with great
deliberate force / struck the fatal blow

a gush of blood spurt out over the table

painting

       a

          line

             of

                red

                  dots

                    across

                    the

                    chest

                    of

                    my

                  mother's

                bleached

              white

           dress

    (my mother always wore white for some reason
  she was very particular about it) i think the stain was
the thing that actually affected her / she nearly collapsed

  the intensity of zuzu's agony diminished until finally he was
    dead / his immobile head soaked in pools of blood / my
    brother andré had blood on his collar and down his sleeve
  the sheik and several of his men had splashes of blood on
  their hands and clothes / there was blood all over the place
    the table looked like the aftermath of a battle

as much as i felt compelled as a child / as a human being / to
cry out and try to stop this thing from happening / i was also
compelled by my training as the son of an ambassador never to
contradict / question / or in any way interfere with matters of
international diplomacy / i was told time and time again that

the arabian delicacy

any such behavior could and probably would result in my
father losing his job / my whole family being imprisoned
maybe executed / such outbursts might even cause the
beginning of a war / possibly even a world war
in which there was a chance that nobody
on earth would survive

the master chef and his two assistants came out and started
cleaning zuzu's lifeless head / they shaved off his hair and then
surgically removed the bones at the top and the back of his
skull / when they were through the sheik asked my father if he
would **please do us the honor of taking the
first bite** / my father (whose complexion by now was as
white as my mother's dress) looked past the dead face of the
monkey / took his finger (you didn't use a spoon or a fork)
and stuck it into zuzu's soft brain / he scooped out a little
piece / put it into his mouth and swallowed / everyone was
given a chance to finger their portion of zuzu's mind / i
remember being surprised at how soft and mushy the brain
appeared to be / it looked like it had the consistency
of cheese / like blue cheese

the time came for my mother to take her share of this great
delicacy / she took her finger and scratched off the tiny tiniest
piece of zuzu's brain / then she put her fingernail to her lips
and fainted / moments later / when she came to / she smiled
a wife-of-the-diplomat's smile / she was pleasant and cordial
she chatted with renewed enthusiasm as if nothing out of the
ordinary had happened / i mean / here was a woman with a
phenomenal ability to *fake it* / both my parents embodied
such incredible restraint!
such incredible skill at playing along

while the arab men and women gouged out handsome
portions of monkey brain with their fingernails / my brother

was bent over / discreetly vomiting into one corner of the tent (i didn't know he had it in him) my father apologized / saying that my brother had picked up some kind of viral infection a few days earlier in riyadh and still hadn't gotten over it / at which point all eyes landed on me / there was no way out my twelve-year-old mind interpreted the evening's fiasco on a global scale / the responsibility for doing the right thing rested on my small shoulders / i had to be the one to prevent terrible consequences from taking place / i had to save the relationship between these two powerful nations / i had to secure my father's position in the world / i had to be the one to prevent a war from breaking out / i had to rescue the entire population of the earth and all its animals and trees and oceans and mountains and deserts and all of everything from being blown to smithereens / i couldn't just mush the zuzu brain around on my plate / or throw it under the table / **i had no choice** / i lifted my quaking / shaking index finger and dug it into zuzu's brain / i put my finger into the brain of the little monkey / the little pet monkey / who just a few hours before had played catch with me and put his arms around me and made me laugh / i stuck my finger into the brain of **the only friend i had in that shit hole of a desert!** i made believe i was reaching for a really choice piece of zuzu's brain / then i scooped my finger directly into my mouth and sucked it clean (i really didn't take anything / there was nothing on my finger there was nothing in my mouth / except for the sickening odor of compliance and the rotten taste of betrayal and deceit) i chewed / i swallowed / i even cracked a smile of approval i *made believe* that night / i learned how to really *make believe* that was the night i learned how to really *fake it* / how to bite the tongue that needs to scream / that was the night

i became my father's son

man of the world

running away

my father never ever slapped me / we weren't that close
you see / in french you have the *tu* and the *vous* / when you
don't know somebody you call them *vous* / only when you
become familiar can you call them *tu* / and so it was with my
father (my adopted father) i could not *tutoyer* him / i had
to *vouvoyer* him / that only begins to explain
the distance between the two of us

this man they call my father / only once he slapped me
only once / it was our most intimate moment

i was a kid / and like most kids i got into trouble / not big
trouble / the usual kinds of things / you know / i took little
things that didn't belong to me / i stayed out late / i fibbed
i did things you weren't supposed to do / if there was a rule
to break / i often bit the bait / yet my father hardly ever
scolded me / he didn't seem to care one way or another what
i did / i can barely remember him raising his voice to me / i
was the one who was most often upset / i was the one who
worked himself into a feverish pitch over things / and so
on this particular day i was angry about something / i was
pissed off / i can't remember what it was / all i know
is that i left the house in a rage / and on my way out
i slammed the huge front door of the embassy / the door
must've been ten times my size / i don't know how i did it
but i swung this humongous door so hard it went

and the force of the air (apparently) caused a very rare and expensive vase to topple over / shattering into a million

pieces onto the marble floor / the vase was my father's most

recent acquisition / it was a chinese vase from the ming

dynasty / to me it meant nothing / it was just another dust

collector around the house / actually / i didn't even know

what happened / i was probably on the street before the

door had closed / i didn't know about anything breaking

until i returned home later that night / my father just kept

screaming / he wouldn't stop screaming about **the**
ming vase! the ming
vase! the irreplaceable
the one of a kind / **the**
priceless ming vase / i probably

rolled my eyes and shrugged a *so what* kind of shrug / and

then he slapped me **WHOP** he slapped me real

hard across the face just like that! i was

completely stunned / he'd never before laid a hand on me

i called him *espèce de salaud* (a filthy son of a bitch)

that was the first time in my life i called him something other

than *father* / *yes father* / *i'd rather not father* / *can i be*

excused father? so when the words *espèce de salaud*

popped out of my mouth / both of us were surprised!

i was furious ⟷ he was outraged / for a moment we came

eye to eye / i knew that for him the vase wasn't so much a

monetary thing as it was a piece of history / destroyed now for

ever and ever / still / i couldn't understand / i will never

understand how he could get so completely upset over a vase

no matter how valuable or rare / a vase is an object / an

inanimate thing! i was supposedly his son / maybe not his

flesh and blood / but a breathing human being nonetheless

i never saw him get this upset over any harm

that was ever done to me

my father looked at me and saw / i don't know what he saw

maybe he saw a vase breaker / i looked at him and saw a

running away

hypocrite / a man chosen to represent his country in a foreign land / a man bereft of moral compass / unable to distinguish what's important from what's not / looking at each other for that brief moment / we came together in mutual disgust unable to touch / we touched / by way of slap and shards of exploding porcelain courtesy of ancient china / unlikely to scream / he roared / trained not to curse an elder / i spewed profanity / like two dogs of completely different breeds / we came upon each other by chance / we sniffed / we barked our eyes met and now it came to me that it was time to move on / so that night i left / i ran away
and i never went back

i really didn't know that i was leaving home for good / i had run away many times before / over little things / i would sleep somewhere / in a park / or a friend's house / or i'd hide in one of the servant's quarters / and usually after one or two nights i would show up again / it was marvelous fun knowing that everyone in the embassy was looking for me / it was a guaranteed way of getting attention / whenever i would leave i made sure always to return by sunday night / so i would be able to go to school the next day

this time / i decided to stay a few days with my friend coleman / spring recess was just starting / so that gave me a whole week to torture my parents with a disappearance / it turned out that coleman was leaving the next day for a trip to greece with his family / i asked his parents if they would take me with them / perhaps i exaggerated the degree of my father's rage / i played like i was really scared / for some reason they liked me / i don't know why / maybe they felt sorry for me / for whatever reason / they said

okay / you can come with us

so i ended up on this boat headed for greece / i argued with coleman's father / he was the same type of man as my father a foreign diplomat / a hypocrite / a bullshit artist / he tried to convince me i was wrong about my father / he told me that my father really loved me / and that my father was a very respected man / a good man / a gentle man

if i had a plan / it was to stay away for maybe a week / tops! i had no money / no extra clothes of my own / i was a thirteen-year-old kid / i had to be back in school by the following monday / to even consider missing a day of school was out of the question / but when we got to greece / something very powerful came over me / i was swept up in a swarm of people at the port / tourists / merchants lovers / prostitutes / men in uniforms / street performers hustlers / people of all different nationalities zigzagged in a frenzy of commerce / romance / and action / somehow i lost track of coleman and his parents / suddenly / the chemistry in my blood changed / imagine what it must feel like to know that you are dying / that you are about to die / well / i was experiencing the opposite of that / i felt like i was about to come alive / for the first time / i knew (in some strange way) that this was my chance to live / to truly live / for an instant i felt myself a free agent in a sea of nameless faces / i seized the moment and snuck onto a ship headed for france

when we docked in marseilles / i knew that i was home i was never going back to my parents i always felt that france was my real country / france was my home / although i grew up in the middle east and africa / my parents always sent me to france for the summers / they sent me to stay with a nanny in paris or camps in the south of france / i stayed for two summers in a house outside of marseilles that was a home for painters and artists / this place had a tremendous impact on me / to be surrounded by talented people who worked with color / poetry / nuance

running away

and metaphor / people who celebrated sensuality and argued
over moral / aesthetic / and philosophical questions / was
a great inspiration to me (many years later i was able to see
through these so-called artists and their narrow definition of
art and pseudophilosophical ramblings / but at that time they
represented a window onto a new and different life)

without a sou (or a penny) in my pocket / i snuck onto the
train from marseilles to paris / i just walked back and forth
from car to car until finally the conductor asked me for my
ticket / i told him i was with my daddy who was three cars
down / **and he believed me!** i realized i could
do anything i wanted to / just like that / i could go to the
cinema / i could travel / i took advantage of my age / i did a
lot of things free of charge / because people never suspected
that i could actually be alone / there was always some father
some man who paid for me three cars down / at that time it
was out of the question for a european child to be traveling
alone / for a thirteen-year-old boy to travel alone
across europe was unheard of

once i arrived in paris i had very little choice but to go to
my paris nanny / right away she took me to the post office
to make a long distance call / she told my parents where i
was and that i was okay / she handed me the phone
i refused to talk / my parents told her they
would wire her some money / and asked if she would look
after me for a few weeks till i calmed down / weeks became
months / months became a year and then i left / i never told
her where i was going because i knew she was in touch with
my parents / i enrolled myself in school and rented a room in
a house from an old couple / i had my own special entryway
and a small stove / i paid my way / i earned my keep / i
washed the dishes / mopped the floor / cooked / i did
anything they wanted me to do / a few times i went hungry

for days / i had nothing to eat / i remember walking home from school one day in the cold / i was shivering and hungry and a man came up to me and asked **do you know where i can find any boys? young boys?** to tell you the truth / i was tempted for a moment / i was practically starving / i was so hungry and weak / i came very close to saying *look / i'm available / how much will you pay*? but he was an arab / he looked like a saudi / so something triggered in me that said no! don't go with him / perhaps if he wasn't an arab i would have gone off and entered a life of prostitution and drugs and ended up dead or deranged or something / instead i got a job delivering newspapers / at five o'clock in the morning i'd start sorting / by seven the papers were all delivered / by nine i was in school / a couple of months later i got an idea / i tried to make a deal with the distribution manager / if he paid me *twice* as much money i would deliver *three times* the number of newspapers / he was dead-set against it / so i went over his head / the man at the newspaper plant held out his hand and said **okay / you got yourself a deal** / i hired two kids my own age to get up at three o'clock in the morning to do the job / see / i was a tough street guy who grew up in a part of the world where people need to be resourceful and clever just to survive / even though i was privileged i picked up a lot of that resourcefulness / it turned out to be a superb training for a thirteen- / fourteen-year-old boy living on his own compared with pampered french schoolboy bourgeois little piss heads / i was like a weather-worn man of the world these kids loved getting five francs per week that they didn't have to beg their mothers or fathers for / of course they didn't know i was being paid thirty-five francs / eventually i hired four or five helpers like this / they were all up at three o'clock in the freezing icy-cold mornings sorting papers while i would be sleeping and drinking hot chocolate and eating croissants until eight / they were so grateful to me at the end of the week when i gave each of them their five francs

i swear / one of them (two years later) asked me to give

him a recommendation / i used him / i enslaved him and he

asked me for a recommendation! one day one of my little elves

went directly to the newspaper plant and discovered with

horror that nobody knew him there / nobody knew his name

he thought he was employed by the newspaper / he came

back screaming at me that there was no future for him

i studied so hard in school / i did two years in one / i

graduated at the top of my class / even when school was out

i studied / i read everything i could get my hands on / my

favorite book was *les pensées de goethe* (the sayings of goethe)

i took it everywhere with me / i'd read

it in the bathroom / i took it to bed with me / i took it on

the tramway / maybe i got a little ego kick out of it too / you

know / i'd make sure to sit next to the most beautiful woman

on the train / and while everyone else was reading superman

or stupid tabloid magazines / i was reading *les pensées de goethe*

one of my favorite expressions from the book was *sois beau et

tais toi* (if you look good you don't have to talk) my image of

myself was of an ugly dwarf kid / so to compensate i yearned

to be with beautiful / handsome people / as much as i loved

books / i wanted to become a part of that life / that beautiful

handsome life / beyond books / beyond words / inside

the unexplainable mystery of the city

i left the house of the old couple for a little bohemian
apartment in the west bank of paris / i never told them where
i was going / i suppose i've done that a lot / run away from
places without leaving notice or a way to get in touch / as
a child i was carted from one place to the next / and so as a
young man i carted myself around from one place to the next
with no attachments to any particular country or city or house
or job or even family / although i was just an adolescent boy
i lived as a free man in paris / the boundless expanse of
an unknown future my only home

the back of the moulin rouge

shortly after arriving in paris i got in with a group of guys

who were three or four years older than me / i was thirteen

they were maybe sixteen and seventeen / seeing that i was

pretty green to paris / these streetwise friends took me under

their wing / they showed me the ropes in and around the city

when they found out that i was still a *puceau* (a virgin)

they looked upon me as though i had some very rare disease

apparently / to be a *puceau* / to be a *male virgin* was

tantamount to disgrace / to be a *puceau* meant that you were

somehow less than a man / although i explained to them that

i had fooled around with a girl in egypt the year before who

was completely naked / that did not constitute a full-fledged

fuck / so one night my friends took me to the red-light district

to the back of the moulin rouge / so that i could

(with their help) finally become a man

although i was very nervous about this outing (my heart

felt like it was pounding inside my stomach) i was also excited

by the thought of losing my virginity in the famous moulin

rouge / i didn't even know they had a house of prostitution

there / most people when they think of the moulin rouge

think of the famous smoked-filled nightclub that toulouse-

lautrec and picasso and so many other legends of paris were

known to frequent / that's the way i pictured it / and sure

enough when we got there / a gorgeous marquee beamed out

across the front / i heard music and saw all kinds of beautiful

handsome people going in and out / it all seemed very

thrilling and gay / but instead of going right in / my friends

took me around back / around back was a dark little street like

a lot of other dark little streets in the red-light district of paris

up a short flight of grimy steps / we entered the back of the
moulin rouge / inside the faint red light of the square waiting
room / there was no receptionist to greet us / nobody playing
piano / not a girl in sight / immediately i realized that this
place was just a cheap cheap little whorehouse / the waiting
room consisted of a bunch of couches and on the couches were
a bunch of men / about fifteen or so men sitting next to each
other in complete silence listening to this horrendous
screeching coming from behind one of the four closed doors
down a narrow hallway / i squeezed into a spot on one of
the couches and along with my fellow congregants
tuned into the ghastly screams

puant de merde sale cochon!

a woman was hurling insults about someone's stinky smell

you stink! fous le camp get the hell out of here!

a door flung open / the screaming got louder / and a sock
came flying out of the room into the hallway / followed by
another sock / a pair of underwear / and then a mostly naked
man edging backwards out of the door clutching his pants
the woman kept screaming **blah blah blah blah blah** the poor man almost
died of shame / he gathered up his clothes and vanished
then the woman came out of the room half naked / scratching
her ass through her dirty panties in the most vulgar way / all
the men watched her in horror as she crossed the hallway to go
to the bathroom / still talking to herself about this man and
his dirty socks / when she came out she said **okay who's
next here?** all of the men looked at each other nodding
their heads / nobody wanted her / although i was the last
to arrive / i was practically pushed into the room of the
screaming lady / terrified and excited / i closed the door

the back of the moulin rouge

during that brief moment while closing the door / i remember
savoring the thought of finally attaining the most unattainable
fantasy a boy could have: sex with an adult
woman! all the dreams i ever had of seduction and
voluptuous sweaty sex were about to become a reality / i
turned around only to discover this woman / this prostitute
was already completely naked on the bed / she looked at me
and abruptly spread open her feet / her legs parted with the
mechanical precision of a drawbridge obliging a passing ship
the whole thing was so horrifying to me / she didn't undress
slowly / or tease me a little / or dim the lights / it was just all
spread open on the bed / i could see right into her dark vagina
it repulsed me / the whole thing / i can imagine the first time
a girl sees a man's penis it can be a very scary thing / this big
ugly foreign-looking penis / that's what it was like for me
looking into her spread-open vagina / she looked at me like
let's do this thing already / i just wanted to turn around and
leave / but i couldn't / because all my friends were waiting to
hear about my entry into manhood / so i climbed up on the
bed / and put myself immediately between her legs / but i
had no erection / in fact i think when i saw her there like that
my penis actually retracted itself further back into my groin
i felt nauseous / my knees were shaking / here i was this little
boy with this full grown woman / i was like a little nothing
between her legs / i was intimidated / i felt pressured / i was
totally limp / i just wanted to run away / but i couldn't
after all / this was a gift from my friends / i couldn't tell
them *thanks but no thanks* / i couldn't go out there and say
that i was incapable of fucking / so what did i do?

i asked her if it would be alright to touch myself / she says
do what you want / i don't care / i start to
masturbate on top of her so at least i could have an erection
she's probably very beautiful / but the whole experience to me
is so ugly / i don't even think of touching her / i don't

touch her breasts or anything / i'm just between her legs stimulating myself / she keeps saying **come on quick come on** / i feel myself getting harder and harder / i feel that i'm about to come / but i don't want to insult her by coming right on her / so i ejaculate onto the bed / on the outside of her leg / she looks at me / she looks at the little puddle of come on the bed / and lets out

a tremendous

scream

she picks up a box of tissues

and she bangs me over the head with it

whack

very hard

and she says **idiot! tu es venu sur mon drap!**

(idiot / you came on my sheet)

i don't have time to be cleaning sheets all day! blah blah blah

she screams me out of the room just as she did the smelly man

i'm dazed / embarrassed / and thoroughly confused / outside in the waiting room my friends ask me **what happened? why was she screaming?** i tell them *it was great!* i tell them that *she was just surprised that a little boy knew how to really fuck a woman*

they took me out to celebrate my coming of age / i smiled a yellow smile and thanked them / all the while feeling completely traumatized / after all / i had been conditioned to think that a man was dirty / i always thought that to *spray* a woman was to dirty a woman / so i made sure not to get any of my sperm on her / i figured *what a great deal for her / she got paid and i didn't even spray her / i didn't degrade her*

i also didn't want her to get upset / so you can imagine how

the back of the moulin rouge

stunned i was when she screamed at me for coming on her
bed instead of in her vagina / that stunned me / sitting there
with my friends / appearing cheerful / i tried to make sense
of what had happened / and then i figured it out! i remember
thinking that for a prostitute / in the mind of a prostitute
her vagina is public property / whereas her sheets are private
property / her vagina must become just like a tool she uses in
the public domain / her sheets / her rings / her watch / her
car / those are her private things / i felt sad for her / i
figured everything in her life was probably the opposite
of what it was meant to be

as my friends toasted to my new status in society / i secretly
felt ashamed / for them to pay with their own money for me
to become a man / and to have failed / reinforced my fear
that i was impotent / that i would never ever be able to
do it with a woman / because if this (my so-called *first fuck*)
was any indication / it was a far more complicated thing to
do than anything i had ever imagined / for a man to be with a
woman and understand what she's thinking and what she
really wants seemed to me a nearly impossible task

and so / having conquered my first ritual performance as
a man / i shed my boyhood once and for all and
stepped forever into the bewildering world
of mature adult relations

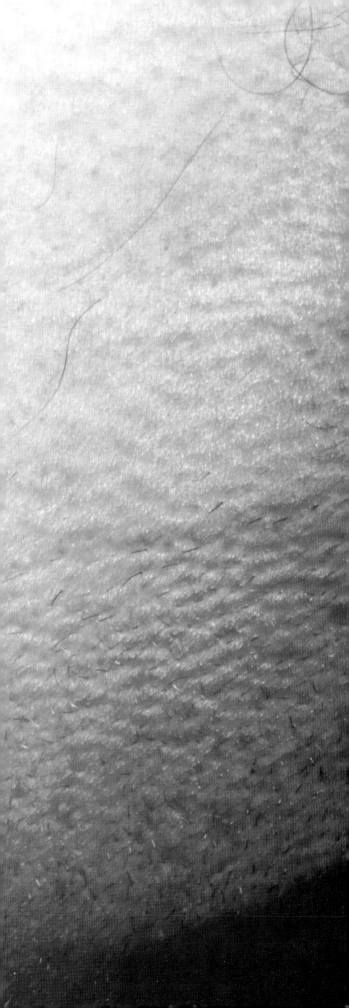

birthright

wings

wings *wings*

god
all i wanted was *wings*

and you give me
a big cock

merde!

the grasshopper years

after graduating as the valedictorian of my high school
with a special certificate in mathematics / i took up the
mandolin and earned enough money playing in restaurants to
enroll in premed courses at the sorbonne in paris / i fell in love
with anatomy / i fell in love with the circulatory system / i
marveled at the way the digestive system worked / pulmonary
function / all of that fascinated me to the core / i devoured
every diagram and illustration and every word of my medical
textbooks / i was particularly taken with the photographs of
split-open cadavers because they allowed me to see the inner
workings of the human body in a way that words
or charts could never do

at the end of my second semester at the sorbonne
i met a young woman about my age who took me to brussels
i wasn't very romantic at that time / you could say i had my
troubles being intimate in a loving sort of way / i enjoyed
having sex but mostly with women i hardly knew

medicine was my love!
my passion

a woman / a living breathing human being was much
harder to love than a textbook or a field of knowledge / i liked
this woman *monique* / and she liked me / i think even if her
father wasn't paying for her apartment i would have moved in
with her anyway / in the fall i entered a six-year program at
the medical school in brussels and became even more obsessed
with my studies than before / i worked day and night / i slept
with textbooks all over the bed / monique was not particularly
crazy about sleeping with all these books / but she preferred it
to my falling asleep at the desk or in the library

my ultimate goal was to become a researcher / to find a cure

for cancer or discover the secret gene for long life / something

that would make an everlasting contribution to humanity

after taking four semesters of organic chemistry i began

spending extra time in the lab experimenting with different

substances / although i wish i could tell you that i discovered

a miracle cure for some horrible disease / what i actually came

up with was an edible polymer / which when combined with

starch and some sugar made a nice little chewing gum / i

could give it a bright color and add some fruit flavor and *voilà*

people liked chewing this stuff!

so this lebanese businessman got together two other investors

and we started a chewing gum factory in the bekáa valley

towards the middle of my third year of medical school i started

losing interest in studying the body / in fact i started to hate

anything having to do with body mechanics / surgery / organ

dysfunction / all of that became predictable and uninspiring

to me / the heart / the lungs / the kidneys / none of it

seemed mysterious any longer / i yearned for something

deeper / the only organ left that really fascinated me / that

still seemed almost totally mysterious to me was

the brain!

so i took a leave of absence and was admitted to

the psychology department at the american university in

beirut / every week i traveled back and forth from the chewing

gum factory in the bekáa valley to the university in beirut / i

loved psychology! like a sponge i absorbed all the personality

theories i could find / abnormal psychology

child psychology / human sexuality / the physiognomy of

the brain / experimental psychology / no matter what the

class i'd always ask a million questions / the professors liked

my enthusiasm for their subject / but i got a very strong

impression that my fellow students found me overzealous

the grasshopper years

the problem with studying any of the sciences in an academic environment is that it's mostly rote learning / at best it's theoretical / rarely do you get to apply the knowledge you're acquiring / after a while it becomes boring / very boring assimilating facts / regurgitating them back to the professors my hands itched to actually **do** something / to actually make something / so i started painting on sundays / every sunday i would make four or five paintings / eventually i painted almost every day / my apartment became an obstacle course full of paints and brushes and canvases / instead of falling asleep with my books / i fell asleep on my paintings

one day i discovered that if i added heat to the same plastic polymer that i used in my chewing gum / it changed the double bond of the polymer into a benzine ring which could then be attached to an aniline or a pigment / this allowed me to paint directly with plastic and use as many different colors as i liked / i called my invention *The* **kobalith**™ as far as i know i was the first person to paint with plastic in more than one color / usually you'd see red plastic or brown or yellow plastic / but up until *The* **kobalith**™ it was always a one-color deal / when i applied this multicolored plastic to a piece of paper or a canvas i got this incredible cracking effect / because when the plastic shrinks / the bonds shrink / and then it cracks in a million different directions **it was a fantastic effect!** but then i worked very hard to make a painting out of it / *The* **kobalith**™ was a process that induced chaos / and to control something that's inherently out of control is very difficult / i sprayed it i splashed it / i used all types of brushes / electrical brushes air brushes / sponges / anything i could think of to control the cracking effect / i made these enormous paintings / at first they were just experiments / after a while they were extremely popular / my first one-man show was hailed in the papers as being **"revolutionary"** i remember one reviewer wrote **"debs will probably grow to be one of the great artists in the field of abstract expressionism"** i didn't even know what abstract expressionism was! that first show sold out within two days of the reviews / it brought in a fair amount of money too / and do you know what i did with all that money? i gave it all to a friend who needed money to go to dentistry school / it paid for his first two years of tuition and room and board / it was the first time i ever did anything that made a major difference in the life of another human being / the minute i gave him the money i made a point to disappear from his life / when you make a gift like that to someone you must lose them as a friend / because when someone owes you so much / the relationship is forever changed / i wanted to spare him that feeling of debt / several years later i bumped into him and he thanked me so much / he wanted to be friends with me again / he gave me his address but i threw it in the garbage / believe me it was a sacrifice not to get together with him because he knew a lot of girls

suddenly i was a hot commodity with art agents in france and lebanon / for about six months my picture showed up in magazines along with favorable reviews / i was actually making a lot of money on my paintings / but i didn't care about the money / i didn't care about the notoriety / the only thing that i got out of this brief success in the art world was an entrée to women / this is what i used to do: after a review would come out in a magazine or a newspaper / i would stand next to a kiosk and look for beautiful women (i kept an eye out for tourists / because a french woman would just slap me) i'd approach the woman and tell her that i wanted to paint her / if she questioned me / like **how do i know you're really an artist?** i'd say *well* / *if you don't believe me just check out the newspaper in the kiosk* / nine times out of ten she would be

the grasshopper years

very impressed / because a lot of women come to paris looking for a good time / looking for artists and the bohemian scene it didn't seem to matter that i was short and ugly / they were happy to meet an artist / not only an artist but a legitimate one with a reputation / it was the mid-seventies / these girls were on vacation / they wanted to get laid / i wanted to get laid / it was perfect for me because i didn't have to get too close to anyone / it was during that period of time i started to develop my fetish for asses / my difficulty with vaginas never really went away totally / asses seemed more approachable to me / more animal / less intimate / asses were perfect / perfect asses were even more perfect! if i walked into a room or a gallery or a library / i looked for the perfect ass / the following year i had two solo shows / one in paris and one in lebanon / at my opening in paris i met three women with beautiful asses i remember i spent one night with one and the next night with the other two / it was amazing! meanwhile i was still a student of medicine and psychology / the first day of the spring semester i walked into my class in advanced human sexuality at the american university in beirut / and i immediately noticed the most amazing / scrumptiously delicious ass i'd ever seen / well it turned out that the woman who possessed this ass was also the most brilliant woman i had ever met / i fell in love with *marizette* on the spot / we started doing everything together / we moved into an apartment together in downtown beirut / we took a class in english at the john f. kennedy center / then after i finished my psychology degree we moved to america so marizette could earn her ph.d. in parasitology at purdue university / i looked forward to starting a new life in the states from scratch / after purchasing the airplane tickets i only had a few thousand dollars left to my name / i should have been a millionaire! but both my art dealers turned out to be crooks / they ripped me off for a lot of money / and to add insult to injury the palestinians invaded the bekáa valley

and turned my chewing gum factory into a warehouse for

ammunition / they also took over the banks / one day they

just rolled one of their huge tanks into my bank and blasted

open the safe

kaBOOM

just like that . . .

insurance companies stopped honoring any claims for lost

property or savings / the embassy just kept saying

in a few months the civil war will be over

and everything will be back to normal

in a few months / it's been almost twenty years now

and they're still saying the same thing **in a few months**

in a few months / the deed to the land we built the

factory on is actually in my name / i can show you the deed

but what am i going to do? go to mr. arafat and say

excuse me sir / according to this

piece of paper here . . .

marizette and i were very much alike / too much alike

probably / we were like two positive ends of a magnet / she

was also french and had spent many years in the middle east

she was the only person i ever met who would walk barefoot

in the snow / she was incredibly intelligent and opinionated

we argued a lot over movies / books / anything / the

time of day! our fights were very passionate

everything we did together in the beginning

was fiery and passionate

just as soon as we were all settled into our apartment in

lafayette indiana the landlord found out we weren't really

married / he told us **IF YOU DON'T GET MARRIED**

YER GONNA HAFTA LEAVE MY PLACE / **IF YOU GET**

MARRIED YOU CAN STAY AS LONG AS YOU WANT

the grasshopper years

we didn't want to get married / we both loved each other a lot
we were together / we didn't need a certificate to prove our
devotion to each other / but we talked about it and decided
to do it / it wasn't even that great an apartment / it was just
a small one-bedroom / but who wants to move when you
can go to court and sign a piece of paper in a half hour?

so that's what we did / but / just before we left to get married
we got into a terrible argument / we drove all the way to the
court not speaking to each other / i was talking with my
witness and she was talking to her witness / and the two
witnesses were talking to each other / but marizette
and i wouldn't even *look* at each other

when we finally got to the court / we went into the judge's
chambers and he started the proceedings / he asked me some
questions and i answered him / then he asked marizette some
questions and she answered / but the two of us weren't
responding to each other / it was obvious something was
terribly wrong / **and he knew it!** he could
see that **those guys are not even
looking at each other** / a blind man
could have seen that / so when he got to the part of the
ceremony when he asks *if anyone knows of any reason why
these two people should not be lawfully married* / he waited a
long long time for someone to say **okay wait a minute
there's something wrong here**

but nobody said anything

so we were married / we drove back in complete silence
the next day we were lovers again / all kissy kissy and wrapped
up in our lives together / and then a day or two later we were
at each other's throats / it was a stormy relationship
especially in those first few years together

when i was growing up in the embassies / i discovered (when i was very young) that i could get whatever i wanted if i started to make a scene / like lock myself in the bathroom or break something / or threaten to break something / everybody just said **oh my god** / **okay** / **okay** / **don't do that claude** / **let him have it** / **whatever it is he wants** / as long as it wasn't a ming vase or something like that / if i broke the smallest little thing they would just let me have my way / they couldn't afford to have scenes and broken dishes / it was very effective / so after a few years of losing argument after argument to marizette / i decided one day to try what i did as a kid / we were having a fight over something (something stupid i'm sure) i got really mad at her

so i took a cup that was on the kitchen counter

and right in front of her i smashed it

onto the floor

i figured that was the end of the argument

marizette looked at me / then she went to the cupboard

grabbed a plate and **smashed** it onto the floor

which was very unexpected / i was shocked actually

then she took out a bowl (like a big salad bowl)

and did the same thing

WhacK

right onto the floor

until one by one she threw every single piece of china

we owned onto the floor / every single dish / every single cup / every single glass and saucer / smashed into a million fragments / most of those things we brought from overseas together we packed each piece very carefully / wrapping them in newspaper / putting them gingerly into bags and then into boxes / not one piece of glass or ceramic survived the massacre

the grasshopper years

you know i never pulled that trick again / it's not that i didn't

want to / but who could afford it? once she slammed the

door in my face like **wham** / i couldn't

stand it / **that was my technique!** nobody

ever pulled those things on me before / with marizette i tasted

my own medicine / and i loved her all the more for it / for

standing up to me / after a while / if i got really upset about

something i just held my breath / i held my breath

a lot when i was with that woman

from day one of our relationship / marizette and i worked on

defying the traditional canons of what it meant to be a couple

having met in a course on human sexuality we were very

conscious and respectful of each other's needs as sexual beings

we prided ourselves on breaking taboos / the mid-seventies

after all was an age of experimentation / when we got married

we vowed to make our life together a successful experiment in

open marriage / we actually signed a contract to that effect

the only stipulation in the beginning was `total honesty`

whatever we did we had to tell each other all the gory details

in fact / we wanted everything documented so that one

day we could publish the results of our long / happy / and

groundbreaking union / together we set out to prove that a

couple could love each other deeply and yet be promiscuous

our goal was to transcend what we thought of at that time as

the common propaganda on marriage and the primitive

emotion called *jealousy* / we actively worked on pushing the

boundaries to see what we could take / one day marizette

asked me if i could take it if we invited her teacher over for

dinner / and i cooked for him / and then after dinner i left

and she made love to him in our bed / as painful as it was

i went along with it / a month or two later we agreed that i

should sleep with her best friend / and then (believe it or not)

i actually slept with her sister / eventually we realized that

we were hurting each other / so we amended our contract

by adding another restriction: <u>no sex in our own
bedroom or our own bed with anyone but each
other</u> / we cried in each other's arms / happy that we had
created a private space / a sacred space just for
the two of us / a few months later we had to amend again
<u>no sex with neighbors or friends or relatives</u>
sacred again! then it widened to not having sex
<u>with anyone living in the same town</u>
and then <u>the whole city</u> and then
<u>the whole state</u>

i have to admit that indiana is not the most stimulating of
places i've seen on this earth / i'm not a beer drinker / i never
got any enjoyment out of cheering on hoosiers as they chase a
ball around a stadium / and i'm not one for watching the grass
grow on endless stretches of flat land / so to occupy my time
i took whatever money i was making off a line of greeting
cards i designed / and enrolled in the art program at purdue
university / yes / i was for a long period of time what you
could call *a perennial student* / my insatiable curiosity kept me
jumping between different fields of science and art / at the
same time i envied people who could sustain a tunnel vision
for an entire lifetime / staring down the same microscope for
thirty / forty years / painting canvases in the same style year
after year with just the slightest changes in color palette or
thickness of brush stroke / i admired people who could
convince themselves that through a very narrow set of
concerns an entire universe could be found / i related to that
singularity of focus whenever i was in the midst of earning a
degree in one thing or another / i became obsessed with
whatever i took on / but it was as if i was born with a gene for
the restless mind / *a grasshopper mind* / as soon as i felt
i understood something to the core / i was attracted to its
opposite / the opposite hemisphere of
the brain / to this day the struggle between art and

the grasshopper years

science is waged continuously on the battlefield of my soul occasionally there is a summit and the two work together in unison / but for the most part / science and art couldn't be more different / being a student of art is a much less precise activity than being a medical student / in both fields you can work with technology / you can study anatomy / the human body / even chemistry / but in art you can step back and say *aha! look at that! behold! that is a thing of beauty* / if you take the time to do that in medicine you just might have a dead patient or a failed experiment on your hands / also you can't really rise to the top of your class in art / because who's to say? i can spend a month working and reworking a painting or a sculpture and bring it into class / and some other guy can piss on a canvas the night before it's due and who's to say which is a better work of art? it's even possible that his piss painting is somehow superior to the thing i toiled over / after all / he is a superb pisser / the control of his aim / the gesture and sweep of his line / the uniformity of his color *bravo* **bravo** **bravo!**

there came a point where i simply had to leave indiana because there was a little too much pissing going on / i mean i might be an arrogant son of a bitch / but i know piss when i see it / i live / i see / and i judge / and either it's garbage or it's genius / garbage or genius / but it's hardly ever genius almost never is it genius / which means there's a lot of garbage out there / garbage garbage garbage garbage garbage / mostly there's garbage / either it's totally totally totally great / or it's garbage / and it's usually garbage / look / you can say what you want / you can say **but claude** / *isn't there such a thing as very good? isn't there a middle zone? a gray area?* and i will say to you *you're right ! you're absolutely right! there is a gray area / there is a middle zone and i found it in indiana* go ahead / go ahead / call me an arrogant son of a bitch / but i know what i know / and i knew that i had to leave indiana or i would dissolve into an eternal unstretched canvas of piss

as i was finishing up my b.a. degree in fine arts at purdue i decided to apply to the graduate program in graphic design at yale university / when i asked my art professor (this old painter with a long white beard who was fucking every girl student he could lay a hand on) for a recommendation / he told me **you have one chance in a hundred thousand of getting into yale / and because your chances are one in a hundred thousand i don't want to give you false hopes by writing a recommendation** / he said this to me in a very paternal way / he liked me a lot this guy / he told me he considered me one of the best students he ever had / i got A's in all his classes / but his philosophy was **not to aim too high / that way you don't get disappointed**

so i was stuck / what was i going to do / ask my organic chemistry teacher in lebanon to write me a reference for art school?

on the merits of my slides alone i managed to get an interview for two weeks i polished up on my english / then flew to new haven connecticut / showed my portfolio / answered all the questions they threw at me and left the interview certain i'd made it into the program / but instead of being elated i felt completely depressed / i walked around in a strange funk underneath the neo-gothic architecture of the yale campus until i came to a cathedral / and although i'm not religious in any way (i don't believe in god / i don't pray / i don't do any of that) i went inside just to collect my thoughts / i sat down and started thinking about how i always project myself all alone into new places / all over the world / but this time / this time i was in a lose-lose situation / if i didn't get accepted to yale i'd be stuck in indiana for another two years till marizette finished her doctorate / if i did get accepted i'd be separated from my wife / and anyway i had no money i couldn't afford to get another degree / let alone at an ivy league college / i was consumed with self-doubt and uncertainty about my future / *what can i do? what skills do i have to pay for my studies at yale? after all these years of education and all these degrees what am i really able to do? what am i going to do?*

as i was thinking all this i started to cry a little / i thought i was the only one in the cathedral until a man rested his hand on my shoulder and said **WHAT'S THE MATTER SON?** i told him that *i was probably about to be accepted into graduate school / but my wife wouldn't be able to come with me and i didn't have the money and i couldn't figure out how to make it work* / he asked me **WHAT DO YOU DO? / WHAT ARE YOU STUDYING?** i told him *design* / he said **WELL I'M THE REVEREND OF THIS CATHEDRAL AND A PROFESSOR AT THE DIVINITY SCHOOL / CAN YOU DESIGN ANYTHING FOR ME?** i looked at him and said *i . . . i . . . i could design all new robes and vestments for you* (even though i was specializing in graphic design / i was sure i could design anything including robes / why not?) so he said **IF YOU COME TO NEW HAVEN TO GO TO SCHOOL AND YOU DESIGN ROBES FOR ME / I WILL MAKE SURE YOU ALWAYS HAVE A FREE PLACE TO LIVE** flying back to indiana i wasn't quite sure whether i had seen an

apparition or what / any other person would have considered

my encounter with the reverend a true religious experience

if not a miracle / i'll tell you for a moment there

it even made *me* wonder

i told marizette that now that i was a yalie i would use

whatever influence i had to get her into the yale medical school

so we could be together / we disagreed about the value of the

doctorate she was earning / she wanted to go to africa and

study parasites / i felt us drifting apart / i wanted

to scream / instead i held my breath

at yale i applied my skills in drawing and painting to

designing posters and books and things like that / like always

i didn't get along with most of my other classmates / but if

i got anything at all from yale it was meeting my soul-mate

friend / a whacked-out one-of-a-kind guy named warren

after a day of walking and talking in and out of the rain

we made dinner and toasted *to friendship and many many*

more rainy sundays together / we spent a lot of our free time

together / sharing our deepest secrets / memories / and

dreams / we argued over our diametrical views on sexuality

we laughed and laughed sometimes till the sun came up / he

didn't like it when i'd say *good night* / he took that to mean

let's stop talking now / so i learned not to say good night

my only regret about warren has always been

that the son of a gun isn't a girl

now that marizette and i were in a long distance relationship

we added another amendment to our marital contract

`whatever we did we had to put in writing`

we sent these long letters to each other chronicling our

respective sex-capades / i tried to get her to agree to a

`no kissing on the mouth rule` (with anyone but

the grasshopper years

each other) but she wouldn't agree to it / i made it my own

personal vow to her / and i stuck to it / i stuck to it a lot

for the first six months in new haven the church put me up in

an unused classroom with a small army cot / after showing

the reverend my first few robe designs / he was delighted / he

immediately moved me into a gorgeous old four-story house

it was more like a mansion / with something like thirteen

bedrooms and four bathrooms / there were

rooms in there i never even found!

did you ever live alone in a really large house? it's spooky

it can make you feel all the more alone / sometimes i couldn't

get to sleep / listening to every creak and phantom sound

so i'd do whatever i could to have someone in there with me

i'd ask warren to stay over just so i could get some sleep / but

we'd stay up all night talking / i also used that house for a

lot of sexual rendezvous (i hardly slept for a year and a half)

i challenged myself to sleep with a different woman in every

room / i didn't quite meet my challenge / not for lack of

women / it was more out of bed preference and laziness i

suppose / i threw a couple of wild parties in that house too

i even had an orgy one night with about five guys and ten

women / when i think about it now i get shivers up and

down my spine / what would have happened if somebody

walked in? i mean / to organize an orgy is one thing / but to

do it in a house owned by the church is so completely . . . so

completely . . . i mean / if it ever turns out that there is a god

and angels and all of that / i'm doomed for

all eternity for the fun i had
in that church house

although the good reverend loved my robe and vestment

designs / the church council ended up rejecting them because

they were *too contemporary and asymmetrical in style*

oh well

by the time i graduated with my m.f.a. i managed to convince
marizette to go to medical school / i did whatever i could to
get her into yale / even though she probably didn't need
much help from me / we moved into a small apartment in
the married student housing complex at the medical school

over the six years of our marriage my love and admiration for
marizette only grew deeper and deeper / the more i loved her
the more incapable i was of pleasing her as a husband / in time
i saw her as a sister / a mother / a best friend / but as a lover
i couldn't sustain an interest / the restrictions on our open
marriage contract narrowed and narrowed to the point where
marizette wanted **`total loyalty`** / we tried every variation
of marriage under the sun and it failed / our experiment
was skidding out of control in front of our eyes

in reaction to the grave dilemma of our marriage i wrote
a screenplay called louie / about a man and his penis
louie was the name of his penis / the man loved his wife more
than anything / but after three or four years / like in so many
marriages / he lost interest / having a high testosterone count
sex was too important to him to just let it go / and his wife
was even more important / so he did everything he could to
reconnect his libido to his wife / he undertook a severe
behavior modification program so that he would feel pain at
the sight of other women and only sexual pleasure at the sight
of his wife / he tried all kinds of things / but nothing stuck
no matter what he did he couldn't sustain a sexual attraction
to his wife / the screenplay goes on to contrast the differences
between a man and a woman's sexuality / the man being
turned on by the lure and mystery of new flesh / the woman
only really being comfortable sexually after years of knowing
a man / loving a man / the tragic conclusion to the screenplay
is that these two experiences of sex and love are irreconcilably
opposed to each other / the day i finished the manuscript i
gave it to marizette to read / when i came home later that

the grasshopper years

night she was sobbing on the bed / she asked me *do you believe what you wrote in this thing?* / i told her *i believed every word of it* / she said **then i couldn't possibly live with the author of louie** / i jumped up from the bed and grabbed all twelve copies of louie (including the original) and threw them into the garbage *there* i said *i can't be the author of louie because louie doesn't exist!*

but it was too late / without knowing it / marizette probably had the most remarkable reaction in the history of reading screenplays: *she asked for a divorce*

i offered marizette all i could / i begged her to reconsider i promised her a lifetime of affection and tenderness / but she wanted more than that / and so she left medical school and she left me / for africa / with another man / in search of fidelity / passion / and parasites

i mourned the loss of marizette as though it were a death i mourned the miscarriage of our once splendid experiment when i opened the envelope and read the certificate of divorce i wept / i felt betrayed / i felt like a failure / so many of the things i cherished or worked so hard for flashed before my eyes flashed in and out of my life / a hope / an idea / a promise a chance at making something new and different / a chance at becoming part of something outside of the enduring separateness of *i* the earth is moist and fertile / the grass grows in the direction

of the sun / fields sway to the disposition of the wind and

moon / a dry spell turns to drought / lost — a grasshopper

jumps in random patterns in and around a patch of dirt

i should get a medal

some things stick with you
your whole life
whether you want them to
or not

remember i told you about brother felix / well there's

something he always used to do to me that i've never been

able to shake / he used to stroke my hair *gently* / stroke it and

stroke it with his hand / and then all of a sudden he'd yank

it / he'd yank my hair really hard / one really quick hard

yank / and at that precise moment i could tell he would

ejaculate in his other hand / i remember always looking

forward to the yank / because i knew just as soon as

that happened / he would let me go

that one particular thing that brother felix did scarred me

it affected me perhaps more than any other incident of abuse i

experienced as a child / so much so that some thirty years later

i almost did the same thing myself to a kid / a helpless kid

i was working on a project (let's call it project x) with this guy

(let's call him joe) and in the course of this project we had to

travel around together for a few weeks / me / joe / and his

thirteen-year-old daughter (let's call her shelly) well / i'll get

right to the point here / because this is hard for me to talk

about / but it's important / it's crucial!

one night / the three of us were staying at a hotel together

and joe was out on the town somewhere (i don't know where

he was) and shelly fell asleep next to me on the bed watching

t.v. / she looked very sweet lying there bundled up in a ball
so i patted her head by stroking her hair / what started as an
innocent gesture of affection took me by surprise as i felt
myself getting aroused / i kept stroking her gently till i felt
like i was going to come inside my pants / and then i almost
pulled hard on her hair / i almost yanked her hair / and
thankfully / thankfully / for some reason i stopped myself
thank god i stopped myself / nauseous
i went into the bathroom making sure to avoid seeing my
reflection in the mirror / feeling ashamed / i sat
down on the toilet and cried a little

a few nights later / in a different hotel room somewhere
shelly fell asleep again / suddenly i felt tempted to stroke her
hair / i thought *if i don't yank on it* / *if i don't pull her hair*
she'd never know the difference / for a moment i convinced
myself that *it would cause her no harm if she was asleep and i*
didn't yank / and then / as i was about to stroke her head
something stopped me / a voice inside said
not one stroke claude! not one stroke!
this isn't innocent! this isn't right!
because instinctively i knew the difference between right and
wrong and thank god it overpowered this other impulse
this learned response / this memory that still lives
deep inside my body

i've often wondered *what is it? what is it that makes me*
different from brother felix? he should have known the
difference between right and wrong (that was his profession
for god's sake) he should have been able to stop himself
but he didn't / i stopped / i stopped because somehow
somehow i knew that even in her sleep / even if she never
woke up she might in some way be affected / she might in
the deep recesses of her subconscious know that she was being
used / and it could change her life forever / and that if i

i should get a medal

continued this stroking business it probably wouldn't have

stopped with that / the next time maybe she wouldn't have to

be asleep / and then after that i'd make a little game out of it

telling her that it's our little secret / i can hear the words like

it was yesterday / i can hear brother felix saying

this is our little secret

just between the two of us

imagine a giant loathsome monster steps into the soft

malleable soil of your innocent childhood / leaving a huge

ugly footprint / now imagine the powerful force it has as it

pulls at you from deep inside your full-grown body / a force

that tries to make you act against your own will and sense of

right and wrong / imagine the strength it takes to fight

against such a powerful imprint / you want to erase it

but you can't just erase it / it's three-dimensional!

you can't take a pill and make it go away

and you can't just pretend it's not there

because it will overpower you when you're not looking
unless you are extraordinarily sensitive / conscious / and
disciplined / you will never be able to break the cycle of abuse
until it's too late / i should get a medal for
what i did / on my own / without having to go
through years of therapy and deprogramming and self-help
groups / i should get a medal for fighting the beast that tried
to trick me / that tried to overtake me / not judgment
or suspicion / a medal! i deserve a medal
for what i did / for what i didn't do
for what i'll never ever do

slavic escapades

the first time
i ever went to moscow
i brought a suitcase full of presents
a gold engagement ring and dreams
of kalinka swirling around my head

right after marizette left me / i was so devastated i tried to

fill the void with other women / consumed with this feeling of

having failed / having failed at marriage / i was determined to

get it right / for the first time in my life i had marriage on the

brain / if i saw a woman i'd wonder if i could live with her for

the rest of my life / that's what i thought when i met kalinka

there's a woman i could marry! she was teaching russian

literature at yale as part of her ph.d. requirements / i sat in

on one of her classes and fell for her instantly / here was an

independent woman who spoke eight languages / she seemed

to know exactly what she wanted in life / this bulgarian-born

intellectual fascinated me / to tell you the truth / i think she

reminded me a little of marizette / kalinka didn't respond

favorably at all to my advances at first / but within two weeks

i seduced her into my life / then to my surprise i discovered

that underneath all her smarts was a very playful childlike

woman / *woooh* / what a combination!

as soon as we became comfortable with each other

she told me that she was about to leave for russia for a year

to finish her doctoral research which was a comparison of

mythological deep-sea creatures (like mermaids and sea

dragons) in russian versus chinese folklore / i tried to

persuade her not to leave / i begged her to at least put it

off for a year so we could get to know each other more / as
much as she cared for me / she refused to change her plans
her work came first / and so within three months of being
together she was gone / leaving like that made kalinka all the
more attractive to me / i became completely obsessed with
this woman / after eight or nine weeks apart i started to lose it
i was convinced that this was the girl for me / i decided to go
to russia and ask for her hand in marriage / i picked out a gold
engagement ring and all kinds of little presents / packed a
suitcase and flew to moscow / kalinka met me at the airport
we went back to her dorm room at the university
had a huge fight and broke up

so there i was in moscow for fourteen days / i didn't speak
russian very well at all / i knew no one / to tell you the truth
it was just about the last place in the world i wanted to be
but then i discovered that i possessed two very valuable
commodities: *an american passport*
and a very big cock

the slavic women love to fuck / they're very free about it
even the prostitutes act like it's not just a job / which is good
for a guy because you don't feel like such a pig afterwards
every prostitute in the world hates men / in france the
prostitutes don't only hate men / they despise them! if you
grab a leg up during the missionary position / it's an extra
fifteen francs (it used to be fifteen francs / i don't know what
it is now) if you want *en levrette* with a french whore / first
you have to be prepared to get into a big argument / they act
like they're shocked / like they never heard of such a thing

slavic escapades

so you have to beg and beg / of course they always come around / but it's an extra fifty francs / in amsterdam the prostitutes are very expensive / the guilder is very very high and they're not all that beautiful / the american prostitutes act like they're doing you a big favor / **are we done yet? that'll be an extra this / an extra that** / they're very businesslike / they've got calculators attached to their vaginas and there's a big surcharge on assholes / and who can blame them? i shudder at the thought of what these women probably go through in a day / and as a single man / alone somewhere for the first time / knowing what these woman put up with makes you feel all the more guilty about the whole transaction that's why i was so surprised to discover the attitude of the russian prostitutes / they act like they actually enjoy having sex with you / there's practically no guilt attached to it / i was in moscow for fourteen days / and every single day i was with another prostitute / i sodomized this yugoslavian woman and she loved it! just because i told her i was american there was no extra charge / you remember seeing all those pictures of people in the soviet union huddled together in the cold waiting on long lines for rations of bread and potatoes? that's how the women lined up for american men over there **they all wanted to leave!** at least that's the way it was back in 1985 before the collapse of communism almost every woman i met wanted to get out of there and go to america / there was always hope when they met an american man that if they showed you a really good time you might actually come back and take them with you to the states / even though you couldn't just marry a russian woman the first time you're over there and bring her back on the plane with your luggage / they were very strict about that / you had to come back three or four times to prove you knew each other for at least a year before they would even consider letting you take off with one of their women / even so / a lot of women saw western men as their only ticket out / it was very tempting

for the man too / to be lonely and be approached by the most
beautiful women in the world / the romanian / yugoslavian
even the polish women / they're not what you think of when
you picture the stereotype of old roly-poly ladies with black
hair nets / a lot of slavic women are astonishingly beautiful
they have those huge succulent lips
those luscious lips / they're blonde / and they
have those big blue eyes / and those high gorgeous cheekbones / but most importantly the slavic women know how
to have fun / for fourteen days i had my pick of the litter
except for the last night / the very last night i wasn't with a
prostitute / i knew i had to spend whatever rubles i had left
so i went to this exclusive nightclub for foreigners / women
from the university and businesswomen would go there
looking to meet men from the west / now usually it's very
difficult for me to meet extremely attractive women / it takes
a lot of work on my part to get them interested / i may be
charming but i'm no john wayne / i'm no robert redford / it
was incredible the reception i was getting from women who
normally wouldn't even give me the time of day / from out of
nowhere the most ravishing and exquisite woman i'd ever seen
in my life comes up to me and motions me to dance with her
this woman was very very feminine / she just kind of floated
across the dance floor in her red low-cut strapless dress and
effervescent smile / she looked like she was straight out of a
hollywood film from the thirties (the opposite of marizette
and kalinka) i thought to myself *maybe it's time to give up on
strong independent women / maybe it's time to be with a more
feminine / eager-to-please type* / she was there with her mother
so i got in good with her mother / because the mother spoke
some french / i treated everyone at their table to champagne
and food / all for a whopping twelve rubles / which was
equivalent to twelve american dollars back then / they must
have thought i was a rich american tycoon / so the mother and
her beautiful / elegant daughter (sashula) took me to their

apartment and made me an authentic home-cooked russian meal — borscht and carrots (in moscow they put carrots in everything / carrots in stuffed potatoes / carrots in soup / in dessert / carrot salad) **it was deadly!** it was the worst meal of my entire life / enormous portions! the ethic over there was to feed your men / and these two women were feeding me / so i ate / and i got to thinking *look / you came here to get engaged / you came to moscow because you wanted to get married / and here you are in the house of the most beautiful woman in the world / her mother already likes you / she's sweet / she's very very sweet / she's educated / i hardly know a word of russian and she can't speak english or french or arabic / but what the hell / i'm good with languages / this is too good a thing to pass up* / so i reached into my pocket and took out the gold engagement ring (the ring i never got to give to kalinka) and proposed to sashula right there in front of her sweet overbearing mother / she said yes on the spot / it was very touching / it was incredibly romantic and spontaneous / the next morning they both came to the airport to see me off / it was irresistible watching the two of them crying at the airport as i flew off to america

over the next two months i floated on air / even though it was the middle of winter it felt like the beginning of spring i was in love with the personification of beauty / i was **head over heels in love with this girl** i carried her picture wherever i went / i showed it off to nearly everyone / my friend warren wished me the best / but i could tell he thought i'd really lost it this time / i convinced myself that i could tolerate the mother / she would have to have her own apartment / at least her own room / but she'd cook for us and probably do housework for us / and besides / i always wanted a mother / a mother who would tell me what my wife was saying / and tell her what i was saying / i have to admit the language barrier worried me / it turned out sashula did know a few words of french / but we couldn't get beyond stock romantic sayings and little chitchat about the weather during our weekly phone conversations / so i decided to learn russian i hired a middle-aged émigré to be my private tutor / when she found out that sashula was estonian / she flung her hands up into the air / shook her head / and blathered on about how awful baltic women are / the age-old tension between blue-blooded russians and people from the ethnic provinces boiled up before my eyes / still my tutor was charmed by my story of love at first sight / so she dutifully played her part in this intercontinental romance by giving me the means to speak and write in the language of my future wife

every saturday night at eight p.m. / for two months i tested my progress with this excruciating language on the phone with sashula / we spoke in broken phrases about our love and the plans for my next visit to russia / as difficult as conversational russian was / writing letters was even worse the alphabet is all screwed up / i mean / they use many of the same letterforms / but the letter that looks like a P is a D the B is like a G and the N is upside down / my god it can turn your brain inside out! it's terrible! but my passion drove me to overcome these obstacles / and i managed to learn the language well enough to begin our life together without always depending on the mother for interpretation

for the second time in five months i packed a suitcase full of presents and boarded a plane to moscow / sashula and her mother picked me up at the airport and took me back on the train to their apartment / sashula looked older than i had remembered her to be / i detected the onset of age lines forming at the corner of her eyes / we got into a conversation about music / i found out she didn't care much for opera later in the evening i became a little irritated when she said a

slavic escapades

prayer before dinner / she prayed the last time i was there but for some reason it didn't bother me / suddenly i realized that she was actually religious / **here i come to a country where god is outlawed and i fall in love with a zealot!**

the next day / the mother went out to pick up some food at the store / leaving sashula and me alone for the first time / we took a bath / i discovered that she had the softest skin / it was so soft / **it was too soft!** her ass was like mush! like jello or some kind of pudding or something / i don't mind soft feminine skin / i love that! but she had absolutely no muscle / no tone / no tone at all / *what a disaster! i'm about to get married to mush!* that evening we had a big fight / she threw the ring at me and i never saw her again

once again i found myself alone in moscow with a gold engagement ring in my pocket and fourteen days to go before my flight back / only now i had two ex-fiancées in town / i walked around the bitter cold streets in this half-dazed / half-frenzied stupor / horrified at the thought of having blown most of my savings / my romantic fairy tale up in smoke

russia was a tremendous disappointment all around / here i was a confirmed socialist / an ardent marxist / the grandson of eugene debs / in the capital of the greatest communist nation on earth / and all everyone was concerned about was money / deals / **everybody was on the take** you had to pay everybody off for any little thing / just to get into a restaurant / just to get a piece of bread / and if they knew you were from america / forget it / they'd charge you extra for the air if they could figure out a way to do it / most russians lived a bare minimum existence / they knew as an american you could go into the *beryozka* and buy things that

they couldn't / people paid me to get them cigarettes or
wine / they begged me to send them books when i got back to
the states (even though they knew the package would
most likely never reach them)

on my third night in moscow i had a dream that everything
in russia was completely backwards / people were walking
around backwards / all the lines of people started at the end
and ended at the beginning / when i woke up that morning
i decided to become a capitalist / to hell with lip service for
equal distribution of wealth / public housing / public health
public education / **public bullshit!**
everyone's walking around moscow with a blank look and
a bottle of vodka under their coat / nobody
gives a shit about anybody

there i was in a strange city / in a strange country
completely disillusioned with life / my long-held belief in
socialism disintegrated before my very eyes / within a year
i had lost my wife and within five months two fiancées / i
decided to leave moscow / i drew up a new itinerary / got
all new visas / then i took my suitcase full of presents and the
gold engagement ring and boarded the trans-siberian railway
to lithuania in search of something / i didn't really know
what / i just wanted something that would lift me out of my
depression / something new to believe in / peace of mind
maybe / gorgeous landscapes / a simple uncomplicated way
of life / or just something to grab on to / like / perhaps (if
i was lucky) some beautiful slavic women with free spirits
high cheekbones and big supple lips

three patients

returning home from my slavic escapades

i could no longer hide from the overwhelming despair

i felt over losing marizette

everywhere i turned there was darkness

at the end of every day
i thanked god that i had
one less day to live

finally i wrote out a will / bought a lethal dose of medication

and prepared myself to die / i had it all planned out / i made

warren responsible for disposing my body / but he refused the

assignment and along with his first wife jan helped bring me

back to life through tireless protests and affirmations

still somewhat reluctant / i rejoined the land of the living

the thought of doing graphic design or commercial art seemed

totally repugnant to me / i had to figure out what to do with

myself / i got an apartment and transformed it into a photo

studio with cameras / tripods / strobe lights / umbrellas
backdrop paper / makeup kits / the whole
shebang / i roamed the streets in search of beautiful
women to photograph / my job was to create portfolios that
would launch careers in modeling / several of the girls
i worked with took their portfolios and ended up making a
lot of money in the business / after six or seven months i got
bored with glamour photography / still pictures no longer
interested me / so i bought some film and video equipment
and got involved in a documentary film project about an old
recluse who lived in the backwoods of vermont / although the
film achieved a certain level of recognition and success / the
life of small art houses and obscure film festivals left me feeling
empty / my life had no purpose / no direction / i needed to
make a contribution / i longed to do something meaningful
and stick with it till millions of lives
were affected in a positive way
i decided to go back into medicine / get my m.d.
do research / discover something big
something important!

when i applied to medical schools in the united states
i was openly discriminated against on account of my age
for the first time in my life i was considered *old* (compared to
postpubescent dr. wannabees straight out of college) all of the
programs made it clear that despite my previous training in
medical school and premed / i would have to start over again
from scratch / being in my mid-thirties i wouldn't actually be
certified to practice till my forties / which seemed to most of
these places an unwise investment of time and money for me
and them and society / yet / despite my age and unusual
collection of transcripts i was finally admitted into a medical
school (which will remain nameless for reasons you will soon
discover) when i received the letter of acceptance i threw away
the vial of lethal pills i kept in a dresser beside my bed

three patients

even though it was hard to accept zero credits towards my degree / i adored studying medicine / **i adored it!** even rereading material i already knew was a pleasure / i had the highest grades in my class / all these twenty-year-olds most of them were in it for the money and the security i loved the knowledge / the sheer knowledge!

after about a year i noticed there was a greater emphasis placed on the pharmacological side of medicine than there was ten years ago in europe / and yet with all this talk about drugs it seemed they kept using the same ones over and over again for different diseases / my pathology book was five thousand pages long / filled with all the diseases of the world / yet my diagnostics and treatment book was something like five hundred pages / i kept thinking *there are so many diseases but so few treatments* / all they could come up with was either surgery (cut the damn thing out of the body) or administer one of six different kinds of drugs / sure there are thousands and thousands of drugs on the market / but they're all mostly redundant / and eighty percent of them were discovered by accident / it's ridiculous! **it's not a science / it's bullshit!** even though i became disillusioned with the limitations of the science of medicine / it only bolstered my incentive to make it better / i also discovered a need for radical reform in the way doctors treat their patients / for a few years i paid my way through medical school working at a large hospital as a spy / videotaping medical abuses / i can tell you stories! you could fill up ten books with the things i saw on that job you see / this hospital kept getting sued for malpractice / so the insurance company recommended they spy on certain doctors suspected of being negligent / they hired me because i was a medical student with experience in film and video the hospital had good reason to be scared too / there was gross abuse / they had absolutely no control over their doctors at all

the doctors were like gods / they were walking gods / i
videotaped the suspected doctors from behind walls
and one-way mirrors

one of the first things i videotaped / i saw a man come in for
an intestinal operation / but the doctors took out the wrong
part of his intestine / once they realized what they had done
they tried sewing it back / but it was too late / it was a
bloody frantic mess / let me tell you / nurses
running around / interns panicking / the doctors played it
cool though / the doctors always play it really cool / the
presiding surgeon made sure they threw out the part of the
intestine they had accidentally removed / then he cut out the
small cancer that needed to be removed in the first place
the patient's wife didn't understand why all of a sudden her
husband needed to have a colostomy bag / *nobody ever
said anything about him having a bag for the rest of
his life* / the day after the operation she asked the doctor
why is this bag here? the doctor didn't say anything
about a mistake / only that her husband's condition was far
worse than anyone had realized / the man died six months
later / the man's wife never knew it was due to a gross error
she thought the doctor did the best he could for her husband
she thanked him / she actually thanked him for trying his best
i guess when your time is up / your time is up

the director of the hospital looked at the tapes and said
oh shit / **we really have something here**
he worked out a story with the staff / swore me to secrecy
then very discreetly fired the doctor

imagine how agonizing it was for me to remain passive / to
just sit there behind my video camera like a fly on the wall and
not tell the man's wife what really happened / and not tell the
world / yeah the doctor lost his job at the hospital / but i'm

three patients

sure he went somewhere else to practice medicine / there was

nothing i could do / i signed a contract not to intervene / my

job was to watch and record and keep my mouth shut / so

that's what i did / the same kind of thing happened with

four or five other doctors / it wasn't only the doctors / i saw

nurses give wrong medications which led to horrifying

complications / this happened quite often

after two years of this / it got to the point where i couldn't

just sit there like a fly on the wall / eventually i had to act

that's why i finally got fired / **i reacted like a**

human being! i saw a man dying of cancer / cancer

of the spine / he was in horrible horrible pain / i'd sneak out

from behind my one-way mirror and massage him / i'd make

believe like i was his relative / he had a carcinoma on the

spine that produced gas in his belly / so his belly was swollen

which in turn put more pressure on his spine / that's what

made the pain particularly unbearable / massaging his belly

alleviated some of the gas / he'd groan and moan / i'd rub his

belly / then he'd fart and feel a little better / i did this a lot for

him / he was such a sweet man / i saw his pain become more

and more excruciating / it wasn't sporadic pain / it was

constant (i hope i never have to go through that kind of pain)

he pleaded for more painkiller / **he**

pleaded and pleaded / finally one night

i couldn't take it anymore / i went to the nurses' station and

begged them to give him more morphine / they gave him a

shot every six hours / then every three hours / after that they

couldn't give him any more / they told me they heard him

screaming / but there was nothing they could do / there's

only a certain amount of morphine you're allowed to give in

america and after that it's illegal / because the patient can die

from it / and that could hypothetically bring a lawsuit / so

they keep it at a certain level even though the pain gets worse

it's outrageous! the man is dying! but they'd rather let him die

in pain than risk the lawsuit / this is one of the great injustices
of medicine / i implored the nurses *look* / *i understand all
that* / *but can't you just give him a little bit more? just a
little bit more?* the nurses screamed at me / then they went
back to eating and gossiping and picking food out of their
teeth / while this man was experiencing hell on earth
what an awful way to say good-bye to life

i couldn't take it anymore / so i got the phone number
of the doctor and called him at home / i told him i was the
man's nephew and that my uncle was being tortured

i demanded that he come and take care of him at once

the doctor came to the hospital / i snuck behind the wall
and videotaped the scene / this young hotshot doctor came
into the room pissed off / he was furious that he was woken
up in the middle of the night to come down to the hospital
to look at a dying patient / he put one foot up on the bed
looked down at the old man in a threatening way and said
**you know you're going to die / so don't bother us
we can't give you any more morphine / you're
going to die / let your family be proud of you and
die like a man** / the sick man looked up from his pillow
and said *i know i'm dying but can't you just do something
about the pain?* but the doctor had already left the room

i ran after this so-called doctor and screamed at him
i poisoned his life for three days / i made his life miserable
i went to the office where he had his private practice
i called him at home / i called him *an immoral
vulgar* / *mediocre physician*
i asked him how he could look at himself in the mirror
i wrote a letter to the director of the hospital demanding he do
something about the situation / a week later the director came
and gave me his response / the doctor was not fired / i was

three patients

fired / i could have taken any one of those tapes and sued

the shit out of that place / but that's blackmail

and i'm not that kind of guy

i plowed through three years of medical school in two

years / finally i was able to work with patients directly at the

university hospital / although only in an assistant capacity

it was a pleasure to see patients without a mirror or a camera

in the way / without having to sneak out from behind walls

i was a very happy man to reach the point where the bodies

were not just printed on a page or up on some screen

they were real! this was the real thing!

working in a hospital you get to see people in extreme

conditions / they're tagged as patient number this or patient

number that / they're in / they're out / they're transferred

they die / to keep your sanity you learn to shut off the oozing

reality of these people / you shut off their humanity / just so

you can do your job / so you don't become too attached

even as a medical student i felt myself shutting down a little

but there were three encounters i had with patients that

pierced that invisible barrier and touched me in a way that

changed my perspective on life / although i was there to

help *them* / i think they each did more for me

1

shortly after starting work in a burn unit

a nurse asks me to give her a hand / i wasn't prepared for what

i was about to witness / but for some reason she thought i

could handle it / i follow her into a room and see a very large

youngish-looking man / about thirty years old / lying totally

naked on a bed / right away i notice globs and globs of flesh hanging down where there should have been legs / like a slaughtered cow everything is bloody red / it isn't bleeding but the flesh is raw and very very red / everything beneath his waist is unrecognizable / i look away and then trying not to seem flustered i look again (there is a morbid attraction to death / to dead tissue / that makes a person want to look which explains the incredible popularity of horror movies to peek at raw horror / turn away / and then peek again) realizing that the man is watching me look at him / i fight the compulsion to stare at the mountains of flesh that form the bottom half of his body / i have to make an immense effort to be casual / the nurse helps me enormously because of the very natural and relaxed way she has around this patient / i simply try to copy her casual look / all she wants me to do is help her turn him over so she can apply zinc sulfate to his back i approach the bed / i'm on one side / she's on the other keep in mind the man is large / even without legs he must have weighed 225 pounds / under normal circumstances it would have been hard to turn over a man that size

the nurse grabs his shoulders / leaving me no choice but to lift what's left of his buttocks / **he's so damn heavy!** he's practically impossible to move / all of a sudden i appreciate how legs create a counterpoint to the torso and how without the legs it's almost impossible to turn a body over / the young man is doing everything he can to help us he puts his left hand on the bar and struggles to pivot his weight to the right / the nurse is using all her strength pushing and pushing against his back / i'm trying as hard as i can together we lift him up / up / up / little by little we manage to get this huge guy about halfway up in order to turn him and at that precise moment i discover that his muscles / his gluteus maximus (the major portion of the ass) is still down on the sheets / while the rest of him is at least six inches off the bed **i'm looking at the bone of the ass** above and the flesh below / i have to put

my fingers underneath the muscle / and scoop it up so that it

becomes one with the rest of the body / like forty pounds of

putty / at that moment i look up at his face / he's looking

down at his disengaged body / and then our eyes meet

all of humanity crystallizes in an instant

in his eyes i see an oceanic expression as if he's living in a

dream / an expression of infinite knowing / i'm suspended in

that look / projected into a state of awareness beyond pity

beyond empathy / beyond pain / beyond horror or fear

beyond the highest calamity / it's a moment of pure contact

it is life / it is reality / it's beyond reality / it's beyond

the frame of reference of words

after we left the room i asked the nurse *what happened to him?*

it turned out the man was electrocuted by stepping on a live

cable / the electricity shot through both his legs and out his

arms / i took the elevator downstairs expecting to vomit or cry

it was two o'clock in the morning / i went into the chapel on

the main floor of the hospital and sat down / i didn't cry / i

didn't even feel nauseous / i remember thinking how life

was so delicate / so fragile / so ephemeral / it was a rare

moment of feeling totally connected to humanity

i saw it!
i saw the naked truth of human frailty

not in the rolls and rolls of red flesh / i saw it in his eyes

2

i'm working on the second floor of the hospital one day

when i hear this horrible noise like eııiiıiiııhhhhhhhhhhhh

eıiiiıııiiıhhhhhhh (like a whiny screeching sound of an

animal writhing in pain) e|ɪɪɪɪʀ̌ʀ̌ʀ̌ʀ̌ʀ̌ e|ɪɪɪɪʀ̌ʀ̌ʀ̌ʀ̌ʀ̌

but it isn't an animal / it's a person / i ask the nurse what the

problem is / she says **oh it's just about dinner time**

and 2H wants his dinner / i say *oh okay*

about a half hour later i can still hear the noise going

e|ɪɪɪɪʀ̌ʀ̌ʀ̌ʀ̌ʀ̌ e|ɪɪɪɪʀ̌ʀ̌ʀ̌ʀ̌ʀ̌ / it never

stops / it just gets a little louder and more disturbing / so i

sneak into room 2H only to find a young man coiled up like

a gargoyle / his legs and arms projected out in all different

directions / this guy's completely paralyzed / his eyes are

transfixed to a single point on the ceiling / he must be no

more than nineteen years old / maybe twenty / fixed in

this position forever / the t.v.'s on / but his

gaze is positioned off to the right of the screen / he can't even

bend his neck ten degrees / he's also had a tracheotomy / i

can tell because there's a tube coming directly out of his throat

i can't believe that a person can be such a vegetable / that a

brain such as mine or yours can be trapped in a position of

eternal boredom / i remember thinking that his only pleasure

must be food / what else can he look forward to? i watch him

and listen to his e|ɪɪɪʀ̌ʀ̌ʀ̌ʀ̌ʀ̌ing screams till finally the

nurse comes with his food / but his food is nothing but liquid

of course! it's pure liquid! she pours this

liquid food (that he can't even taste) directly through the tube

after the feeding session he no longer makes the screeching

noise / his body (such as it is) relaxes a little / his eyes soften

i'm flabbergasted because he demanded (for so

long / in the only way he could / with his whiny tortured

voice) he insisted on getting his food / he demanded to be fed

food that he couldn't even taste / it was astonishing to see

that a person would cling to life when there's so little to get

so little to long for / i ask how long he's been in the hospital

the nurse says **seven months** / they've been hearing his

chilling cries for so long / it's become routine for them

three patients

from that moment on / all the miseries of the world were put

into perspective / if this man / this boy could still enjoy life

even when he's trapped in a mangled / unworkable body

if he could live / if he demands and has the will to live

then no one / not one of the six billion people on the planet has a right to feel sorry for themselves complain or nag / no one! least of all me

3

i've always been curious about what runs through the mind

of a person who knows they are about to die / you hope that

their last thoughts are pleasant ones / that they reach a certain

closure / a resolution to their lives / being around a hospital

puts you in contact with many people who are dying and

know it / whenever i could / i tried to get close to people in

that state / you'd be surprised how many people appreciate

the attention / how many human beings die all alone in the

world / even the ones with large family gatherings during

visiting hours appreciate actually being listened to by someone

who just wants to know what they're feeling / i remember one

woman looked forward to getting out of her life so badly / she

said to me *when i go / when i finally die / i won't have*

to worry about my eyesight anymore / or my arthritis

or my overdue bills / or my hardening of the arteries

or how my children never come to see me / or that i

hardly ever get to see my grandchildren / i won't have

to think about the next meaningless election / or how

my husband was cruel to me / how he whupped me

i won't have to relive the moment over and over and

over again when the officer with the gold star and gray

eyes came to the front door to tell me that my son

harold / my first son / my baby / died a hero / i won't have to turn my mind over and over how i could have been a great singer / how i could have married that nice fella / the writer from chicago / how i could have done this or i could have done that but never had the chance or the money or the will / when i go i won't have to bother with any of that

some folks go with peace of mind / but many others have regrets / sometimes they're just small things that get inflated as the person nears the end / there was one man (i had no idea what an influence he would have on my life at the time) who to all the other medical students and interns and nurses and doctors was just another patient dying of cancer / an ordinary man / he meant nothing special to me either / until one day i was in his room when he picked up a newspaper on the table next to his bed and said **look / you see this? seven guys raped this one girl in a bar / they raped her one after the other / they're animals! don't you think they're animals?** he seemed truly disgusted by it / i agreed / i said *it's terrible!* then he looked at me and with a little smile forming at the corner of his mouth he asked **do you think they enjoyed it?** i looked at him and realized that this man was fantasizing about raping a girl / i said *yeah they probably enjoyed it / that's why they should get locked up for a long long time* / i became interested in knowing what a seventy-year-old man who's dying of cancer thinks about / i starting asking him questions about his life his sex life / he told me that he was always faithful to his wife she was very good to him / he never never tried anything with another woman / never ever / only occasionally at the factory sometimes / occasionally (by the water cooler) he would pinch a girl on the butt **but that was nothing** he said / **nothing really** / then he confessed to me that sometimes he'd rub

three patients

against a woman in a crowded train / **but that was it** he said

that was it! / in fact / even though he was a great one

with the ladies / **even a bit of a flirt** / he remained faithful

to his wife till the day she died / i asked him why he felt

compelled to be faithful to her all his life / was it a matter

of choice or guilt or religion or what? he said that he was very

religious and that if he had it to do over again he probably

wouldn't ever get married (which surprised me) and then he

asked me **how does it feel to be sucked?** i was startled by

the question / *beg your pardon?* **how does it feel to have**

your penis sucked by a woman? i thought for a second

and realized he had never experienced this / so i couldn't say

oh it's great man! it's one of the best
things in the whole world / when you
come in the mouth of a woman it's
incredible! instead i looked at him and said

it's terrible / it's awful! her teeth scrape against your

flesh / it's painful / he looked at me in astonishment and

said **oh really?** i said *yes it's really very painful /* he said

you know when i was a young man i had a girlfriend

and this girlfriend / she was married but she was

having an affair with me / and one time we went to this

motel and i was lying on the bed and she grabbed my

penis and started playing with it / i stood up / she was

on her knees / and i didn't mean for it to happen / but

my penis was next to her mouth / so she kissed it / she

actually kissed my penis / like a little peck / if i had

pushed a little / it would have gone into her mouth

seventy years old / on the brink of death / thinking if he had

only pushed a little / the memory was so precise the way he

described it / as though it had happened just yesterday / every

little detail about how he saw the ring on her hand and the

temptation / the scene was so alive

to him / yet it happened fifty years earlier!

he turned around and fell asleep

i stayed there in the darkness of that hospital room thinking about the choices we make in our lives / whether to go or stay whether to act on something or just dream about it / we have our little dreams by god! what's a little dream / a little desire like that? to push a little / he carried that unspeakable little dream around with him for a lifetime this man / his wife wouldn't take his penis into her mouth / and he never ever thought to try / he said **you know** / **women didn't do that in those days** / **you know** / **today they do it all the time**

there he was on his deathbed (practically / he died two weeks later) he didn't talk about money / he didn't talk about some place he wished he'd traveled to / or something he should have said to somebody / he didn't mention anything like that / it was just his penis on the brink of getting into a woman's mouth

i thought about whether i should pay a prostitute to come and suck his cock before he died / but i decided instead to reassure him that it is a terrible experience / the next day he asked me **when you squirt your sperm in her mouth** / **what sort of feeling is it? does she swallow it? does she spit it?** i said *oh* / *they always spit it* / *it's so degrading for a man* / *you don't want to see your sperm on the floor* he scratched his head and said **i see what you mean**

around the same time there was another patient also dying of cancer / colon cancer / who told me in such a passionate way about how he went through life searching for the perfect tits and they were either too big or too low or spread too far apart all his life he spent looking for perfect tits / he never found them / it didn't matter if he did or he didn't / the important thing is having a quest / a search / going out and living a life filled with experiences / so when you're dying you can draw

three patients

on your memories / you can say to yourself *at least i looked
at least i tried to find perfection*

thinking about these two dying (now dead) men / i realized
something about the nature of experience and memory and
sex: it's not the moment of sex that is the most wonderful
it's the *after sex* / not right after / years after! when
you relive the greatest moments of sexuality in your mind / as
if you're watching a movie / you actually see yourself fucking
because when you're in it / when you're doing it / you're too
caught up doing it to see what's going on / to appreciate
what's going on / you know the expression *youth is wasted on
the young* / well i say *sex is wasted on the people having it!*
people today are always saying **be here now** / **live in the
present moment** / WRONG! the
computer of the brain is overwhelmed by
too many stimuli / we can't process a
moment during the moment / but something
that happened yesterday / a moment from
yesterday we can stretch into an eternity

and so i made a pact with myself / to never grow into an
old man wondering **if only** / **if only** / i realized that night
that life was too short / i must seize the moment before it's
gone / and why limit myself to just one moment or two or
three or four great moments / why not have as many
experiences / as many fulfilled fantasies as i can possibly
have in one lifetime to replay in my mind?

yes! yes!
that is the only
way to live
be good / be kind to people / don't
complain / and have as much sex with
as many different partners as possible

and then when i'm sick and dying i'll have so many wonderful memories to rest my mind on

but then i got to thinking about the unreliable nature of memory and old age / so i made up my mind to videotape my sex with women so that when i'm an old man i can just pop in a tape and watch myself in the most fantastic positions with the most beautiful women / so that / so that when i'm old and impotent and i'm dying of impotence / dying of testicular cancer / dying of whatever horrible malady / riddled with arthritis / or just plain old / too old to seduce a woman or sustain an erection / i won't just have one or two memories to savor / i'll have a whole library to choose from / and in every single one there's a different leading lady and in every single one

i'm the star

eternal erection

(holding his penis in hand)

see
this
cock

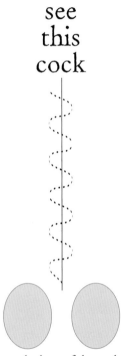

at the base of the cock

my god it looks like an old buffalo!

at the base of the cock there are certain muscles that surround

the veins / the erectile tissue around the veins / and what

they do is / they behave / you see / the parasympathetic

nervous system controls all the involuntary organs / the heart

the whole vascular system / the arteries / veins / capillaries

dilation and contraction / so when the parasympathetic

nervous system (which is beyond our normal control) is

stimulated either by the pheromones (sebaceous gland

secretions) or sensations from the optical nerve / or any

combination of those / it affects the contraction of the veins

and arteries at the bottom of the penis / normally the blood

goes in and out / in and out / in and out / but since there

is a constriction / the blood gets into the penis and stays there
it can't get out / it's a bottleneck situation / this causes a
contraction / the contraction over the vein then blocks the
amount of blood coming out of the systemic circulation / and
since the penis has spongeous layers / the blood infiltrates
those spongy layers and stays there / hence: erection / **the
penis erectile position!** normally thought to
be a condition of limited duration and specific consequence
which is why i began to wonder what the hell was happening
when last night / last night i had this big
this really big erection that

wouldn't go down

i didn't understand / i couldn't figure out why / why it
stayed hard / why? normally after i jerk off / my penis goes
down / **but it didn't!** i got scared / i got scared
that i did something wrong / i don't know / maybe it was the
twelfth time i jerked off since i woke up / which is about
average for me / so i got spooked / i thought maybe i did it
too much / maybe / maybe i finally reached that point when
it just goes *zing* / i mean / because / since i was a little kid
i've never stopped / you know / and now after years and
years of pulling and tugging i thought maybe it / maybe it
finally caught up with me / cause my muscle wouldn't relax
which made me think **maybe it would never
relax** / maybe it would keep the blood sequestered in my
penis forever **and never ever relax!**

i knew i had to do something / so i started to stroke it a little
moving up and down / up and down / jerking it / relaxing
massaging the base (just to relax the muscle)

but it didn't go down

eternal erection

i started getting nervous / i walked around / i paced / i even
started to jog around my apartment

---

but it didn't go down

i thought maybe / if i think of something bad / something
terrible / it would destimulate the parasympathetic nervous
system / so i thought about death / about dying / i thought
about growing old / being stuck with someone
i didn't really care for

---

but it didn't go down

i thought about the terminal patients i worked with in the
hospital / i thought about my arthritis / the expression on my
mother's face when she caught me in bed with my make-
believe-pajama-goddess / my shame and utter embarrassment

---

but it didn't go down

i pictured myself having to go to the hospital / to the
emergency ward with this erection that wouldn't go down
the interns and nurses huddled all around / how would i get
my pants on? / what would i write on the insurance form?
of course this was not job related / but / **just how did
you do this to yourself sir?** i was sweating / my
hands (which are usually perfectly steady and calm) had
developed the shakes / i was trembling / i was actually
trembling / i feared the worst would happen / i feared that
i would have an eternal erection
and that it would never go down / that it would really
never go down! i panicked / i started running
around my apartment / but that only made the thing all the
more tense / i remembered a meditation technique that
warren taught me / but i couldn't remember the mantra / so

i made one up and tried to relax

but it didn't go down

this was it / if it would never go down / that meant that it
could (by definition) never go back up / i almost / i / i was
on the verge of crying when i got an idea / i got an idea that
if i had something cold / something that would draw the
blood away from the penis / it would have to
go down / i ran to the fridge and stood there in front
of the open freezer / my perpetual sin saluting
before the bright arctic light

but it didn't go down

i grabbed an ice tray / pried it open with my shaking hands
and rubbed a piece of ice along the base of my stiff rod

to no avail

although i am a devout atheist / weeping / and in a state of
sheer desperation / i prayed to god / rubbing my stiff prick
with a heart-shaped piece of ice / i prayed to god

my cock began to stand at ease

eventually it dropped / gravity regained its strength / finally
my penis relaxed between my legs like a worn-out ancient
buffalo / red / swollen / exhausted
relieved and happy

if

i think you're charming

warren / i think you're *completely charming* / i do!

i think you're one of the most brilliant / loving / sensitive

creative / fun / attractive guys on the face of this earth / if

i was a woman / i'd want to fuck you / no problem / if i was

a woman i'd give you a blow job right now / wet / slow / soft

fast / whatever you wanted / i swear / i would / if i was any

woman at all / i'd want to marry you in a second / you don't

have to put up with all this bullshit / get out of it!

you can have any woman you want / any woman would fall for

you / everything you touch is special / who could refuse that?

sure they'd have to get used to your smelly farts and your

crooked back and all your psychosomatic illnesses and your

awful snoring and the fact that you don't have any money

most women can learn to live with all that / *you're lovable!*

and that's all that counts / believe me / the second you get out

of this relationship / you'll have girls climbing all over you / it

takes a little work / you can't just sit at home and watch t.v.

but don't worry about it / i'll help you / i'm telling you / if

i was a woman i'd admire you / i'd appreciate your tenderness

i wouldn't give you all this shit / all this complaining and

fighting and neurotic bullshit / you're wasting

your time with all of that / the woman is nothing

but trouble / get out of it / just get out of it

don't be such a coward / you're getting old my friend / you're

not going to live forever / so do something now while you still

have the stuff / if only i was a woman / i'd want to fuck your

brains out / i swear / i would! i'd do it / i'd do it right now

any way you wanted it / i'd do it right now

right now

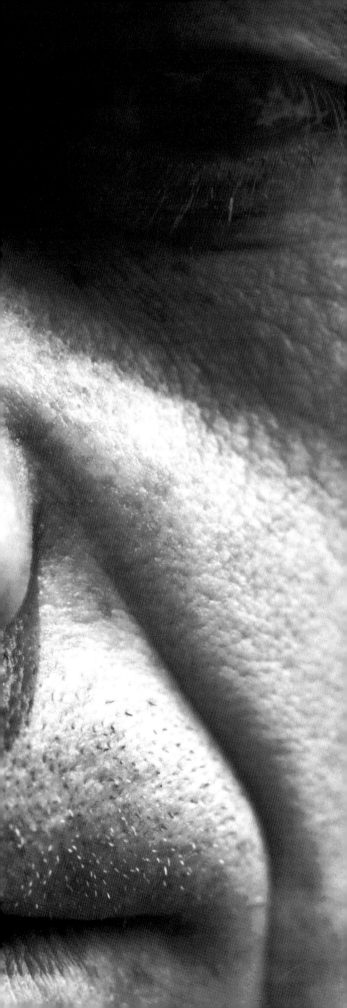

sex tapes

before i show you any of these tapes / i need to warn you
about the kind of sex that really turns me on

first look at me and tell me what you see

no no no no no no no
not like that

first strip me for a moment in your mind
of all the dressing / all the ornaments / strip me / strip me
take off my coat and pants / strip me of my shirt / take off
my shoes and socks / my underwear / even my bow tie / go
ahead / now keep stripping / strip me of all my degrees / and
the four languages i speak and read and write (fluently) you
can take those away / take them! strip me of the years and
years of training i've had in the niceties of human etiquette
strip me of all those affectations / then take away my driver's
license and my credit cards and my calling cards and bank
accounts / take away my social security number and phone
number / take from me my apartment and my rolodex and
my answering machine / strip me of my name / both my
names / strip me strip me strip me strip me till you strip
me down to the bare bare naked essence of who i am
and now tell me / describe what you see

a male human being
fine

and what is a human being?
an insect? a vegetable? an
inanimate object? what is it?

an animal!

that's right!

and what does an animal do?

even a human animal / what does a human animal do?

when you strip away all those other things like waiting for

a bus or applying for a bank loan or shopping for socks or

folding a napkin or taking out the garbage or getting stuck in

an elevator or paying the electric bill or shaving or going to

church or reading a newspaper or sending a mother's day card

when you strip all that other stuff away / what is it we do

us humans? / what are our glands constantly telling

us to do every single day of our lives?

huh? huh?

well i'll tell you / i'll tell you what we do:

eat

sleep

fuck

and whatever else
we have to do
to stay alive

not just for our own sake

but for the sake of the entire species

that's it / that's it man!

those are our entire genetic instructions

all that other stuff is window dressing

now let's go one step further / let's say you take a machete and

you split open my brain / right? just like that

do you know what you would see?

you would see a limbic system

and do you know what the limbic system wants?

all it wants is sex!

that's all the limbic system cares about! and do you know

how big the limbic system is in the human brain?

do you know how big it is?

it takes up most of the brain

it's not a theory / it's a fact

now maybe our species is advancing / as you say / maybe

the makeup of our brains will evolve into something more

advanced / but that's a long way away / maybe another two

to three thousand years / today the human species is still

operating out of the original / out of the raw genetic material

deep deep down we are still hormonally the same / at that low

instinctual level of the hormones / but very few people can

go all the way down there / very few people can go that low
but i do! and when i do / when i let myself get down
there / i become an animal (stripped of all the social graces)
i become an animal who yanks hair / tears clothes / bites
spanks / gets down on all fours / oinks / grunts
howls / fucks ass and loves it!

for an animal / sex is very closely related to violence / sex at
its raw value is a very violent act / *ssshhhhh* / *listen*
can you hear? the horrifying screams of a cat being hunted
down / tortured / and killed by a raccoon / terrifying cries
turn to a kind of resigned purring and then to silence / there
is a death pleasure in those sounds / the pleasure of totally
submitting to another / sex can be like that too / when you're
having great sex and then you come / the whole
world stops / you die / you die a little

now don't get me wrong / i enjoy all kinds of activities that
are distinctive to the human brain / but not many things
shoot off as many neurons in the brain / like when i'm
taking a bath maybe i fire off – 15 neurons
if i'm watching a good film maybe i fire – 70
reading a french comic book – 95
reading virginia woolf – 180
if i see a hummingbird fluttering in front of me – 285
if i'm eating a good falafel sandwich maybe – 300
whereas if i'm eating an excellent pahd thai – 750
if i'm watching a puccini opera – 1500
if i'm playing my mandolin – 2200
playing in a chess tournament – 3500
but when i have an orgasm – millions and
millions and millions and
millions of neuron cells
fire off in my brain
nothing can top that!

sex tapes

sure there are many things / many pleasurable things / some

last longer / some are more refined / more intellectual / more

transcendent / but do they fire as many neurons?

that is the question i'm asking!

i'm not talking about love!

love has nothing to do with what i'm talking about / caring

for someone / tenderness / caressing / hugging / kissing

nurturing / that is something entirely different / because

if i'm with someone i love / like when i was with marizette

i was extremely gentle and romantic / if i'm with someone

i love / i don't fuck her / i'm not like that / i can't sodomize

her or be rough with her / i give to her / i whisper to her / i

kiss her softly behind her ear / i lick her all along her neck

i touch her face softly with my fingers as though i were blind

trying to figure out what she looks like / i massage her feet and

kiss her toes / one by one / i travel with my tongue up and

down her whole body (with the most loving tongue) and if

she wants it / if she wants my tongue between her legs / even

though it's hard for me / even though it's not my favorite

thing to do / i'm there / for as long as it takes / i'm there

for her / giving / giving / giving

why?

because of the cortex!

oh yeah / i forgot to mention that when you split open my

brain / mostly what you see is the limbic system / from the

bottom of the spine to the back of the head (between my ears)

all of that is limbic / but you also see the cortex in the front

it's much much smaller than the limbic system / the crocodile

has a limbic brain / lizards have a limbic brain / rats / but in

addition to the limbic brain humans have evolved a cortical

brain / all humans have a cortex / and it is the cortex that

humanizes sexuality / it's the cortex that produces feelings like

love and caring / that's what ruined my marriage / because
my feelings for marizette became totally cortical / because the
more i knew her / the more human she became / the more
impossible it was for me to lower myself to the limbic level of
the brain / especially if she asked me to get rough with her
my cortex would scream *no no* / my cortex was always
screaming *no no no no way* / whenever she
said **harder claude** / **harder** my cortex would go crazy
my cortex would scream *no*
no
no *no*
no *you can't do that!*
this is a woman
you love!

that's the tragic reality of the two genders / most men cannot
have true limbic sex with their wives after about three or four
years / and most women prefer to have cortical sex until
they're married for five or six years (when they finally feel
comfortable they ask for limbic) the timing is all screwed up

so i hope you're prepared now for what's on these tapes i've
made / because it's all limbic sex / that's all there is / nothing
but limbic / if you want to see *love making* / you're going to
be disappointed / because that's a different thing altogether
love and sex / they're two different entities / and i just wish
you'd finally stop confusing the two

okay that's it / if you're going to give me a hard time / you
can forget about the tapes / i'm not going to show you the
tapes / if you're curious / go make your own tapes

the affair

first i knew this one guy who was married / who needed
a place to see somebody on the side / then i met another two
people who were having an affair / **that's how it all
started** / it wasn't planned / it was a project of mine
i just thought i'd help these people out by letting them use
my apartment / so much of my time was spent either in class
at the hospital or in the medical library / i just figured

why leave a nice place like that empty all day?

after a few months i had four steady affairs (couples) using
my apartment as a safe place to cheat on their spouses / i saw
what i was doing as a way of helping their marriages / because
in my mind / affairs are nothing more than hormonal
discharges / all i did was provide a place for these people to get
it out of their system / so they could live the rest of their lives
without panicking or screwing up / this way they didn't have
to make arrangements with out-of-the-way motels / leaving
secret messages and all of that / they didn't have to destroy
their lives / their families / just to fulfill a curiosity / a
physical need / **i took pride in the service
i provided these people**

in the morning / if i knew a couple was coming to the
apartment / i'd make sure to make the bed up nice with clean
sheets / i'd draw the curtains / leave some flowers in a vase
candles by the side of the bed / and on the bed i'd always leave
something / either a basket of fruit or sometimes a bottle of
champagne with two crystal glasses / i wanted to create an
atmosphere that said *it's okay* / *it's okay what you're doing*
because everywhere else in society they were getting messages

that it was *evil* to have an extramarital affair / it was *evil* to live anything other than a perfectly monogamous lifestyle especially if you're married / my place was an alternative to that / my place was a safe judgment-free environment for people to screw their brains out without all the usual hassles

one regular weekly affair since the beginning was a man and a woman who were each happily married to someone else (with kids and the whole nine yards) it was a hot sexual affair they were having / but then after eight or nine months the woman would come to me and cry that she fell in love with the guy she never meant for it to happen / but she loved him so much she didn't know what to do / she was so consumed with her dilemma / she couldn't work / should they each get a divorce and then get married? but if they did what would happen to the kids? she never wanted to hurt her husband / and all of this / i told her i thought that love should have nothing to do with an affair / *you shouldn't confuse lust with love* i reminded her that all she talked about in the beginning was how incredible the sex was with this guy / now she's talking about love / i implored her to try to keep the two separate

for some reason i became immensely curious about what goes on when two married people are having an affair with each other and start falling in love / i never fell in love with any of my affairs / i wanted to see what it was like firsthand i wanted to see what sex was like in a passionate complex love affair / i wanted to know what people say to each other in a situation like that / so i decided to secretly videotape this couple

shortly before they were due to arrive (on a tuesday afternoon) i'm setting up the video camera inside a deep closet in my bedroom when i hear the front-door lock go *click clack* suddenly i realize i'm stuck / i was planning to just set up the

the affair

camera and leave / but they arrived too early / after a split-second decision to stay / i turn on the video camera / snap off the closet light / hop onto the top shelf / and quietly close the closet doors / leaving only a partial view of the bed / i hear them talking heatedly in the living room about / something about his wife / he's saying how his wife **would be devastated** and she's saying **but last week you promised me you would do it / you promised you would tell her** / and he says / **i tried / i swear i tried / but i couldn't do it / i couldn't get myself to do it** / it's like i'm watching a movie / i can't believe what i'm hearing

after a while they come into the bedroom but they don't do anything for a long time except stand around talking about things like when they're going to tell their spouses / she's saying **you can't do this to me george / i can't believe this! thank god i didn't say anything to robert yet / jesus george / i thought we went through all this you promised you were gonna tell lisa then i was gonna tell george / we've been over this a million times**

in between all these little frictions / they're saying how much they love each other / they're whispering things to each other

he throws his arms around her / they get louder and then

they whisper again / i can't make out everything they say

but i hear something about **getting the money from**

the bank / and something about **joint custody** / and

he says something like **i don't think i can do it** / **i just can't**

do it / but then he says **you're all i think about** / **i want**

nothing else but to be with you / and then finally / after all

this time they sit down on the bed / and they're holding each

other / right? but they just keep going over the same stuff

over and over again / they're crying and scheming and

qualifying their promises and professing their love for each

other / and at a certain point she clears out her nose into the

last tissue of a box of kleenex that was full just half an hour

earlier (what with all the crying going on) / so he says

let me look and see if he's got more tissues

at which point i no longer care about my leg
falling asleep because my heart (which is
already pounding a mile a minute) practically
explodes out of my chest / i'm scared! (the
whole time i was scared they'd find me)
but scared suddenly turns into sheer panic
because what would i say? *i was cleaning the
closet and i got stuck* / *and then i fell asleep*
there's no excuse i could possibly come up
with / all i know is / if they find me / i'll die
i'd be dead / the earth would just open
right up and i would disappear

fortunately he just goes into the bathroom and brings

her some toilet paper / and then they continue crying and

scheming and qualifying their promises and professing their

love / it went on like that for two full hours / and then they

left / that was it! there was no sex / zero!

not a shred of clothing left their bodies

the affair

as soon as they left i just burst out laughing / i laughed
and laughed and laughed / human beings are
so stupid! they can't just enjoy something and keep it
at a certain level / they have to turn a simple thing into
the most wrenching / convoluted experience / i was there
to watch sex / i risked my life to take a peek at hot guilty
passionate sex / instead i'm witness to a human drama / it
was very sweet in a way / very soft / very tender
but it's not what i was hoping for

a few days later the woman comes up to me and says
we can't go on like this anymore / george is
gonna tell his wife / then i'm gonna tell
robert / and ... without thinking i interrupt her and say
i thought george was afraid his wife would be too devastated
she looks at me and screams

how did you

know that?

i say *oh well* / *i'm just guessing*
i'm just kidding ha ha ha he ha ho

she looks at me like **what's going on here?**

if i showed them the videotape in fifteen years / i bet you

they would laugh / first they would kill me / then they

would laugh / they would watch the videotape and laugh

their heads off at themselves / saying all those

stupid and ridiculous things

———

eventually i decided to discontinue my apartment affair

service because all the couples were screwing up / they take

something that is so simple in the beginning / then they

muck it up by falling in love / that's when the balance gets

completely destroyed / they have to get divorced and break

up their families and sell their houses and leave their jobs

and move to different cities / it's a disaster! all i

wanted to do was help people / but they screw up / they

always screw up a good thing / like clockwork / when it

comes to love and sex / people always screw it up

it's over

it's over now / it's finished

i had the courage to make a quick decision / to take it on the chin like a man and just cut the cord / go out / go out there on my own / cut the cord and start all over again / and that's what i did / i suppose / i suppose i could have tried to work it out / i could have stayed and told my side of the story / the facts of the story / but what would have been the use?

it's over now / it's over / i've got

better things to do with my life

after three and a half years in medical school / i buried myself in the library / most of my classmates were worried about passing the boards / i was worried about getting the highest score in the country

over the summer i met a nurse from the hospital / *rhona* after a few weeks together she moved in with me / our relationship was very / how should i put it? mild / very mild that's how things were with rhona – very undemanding there wasn't much time in my life for anything other than studying and coming home to an undemanding relationship it was fine / it was fine for what it was

one night early in the fall / i was walking home from the library (it must have been two or three in the morning) when i came upon two people / a man and a woman with blood all over them / there was a large gash / an open wound across the man's face / blood on the woman's back / there was blood on the ground / **there was blood all over** the woman was conscious but she seemed completely out of it

i asked them *what's going on? let me take you to*

the hospital / they both said

NO

no

NO

no

DON'T WANT HOSPITAL

no hospital

NO HOSPITAL

no **NO**

i said *okay okay!*

can i take you somewhere
where i can wash you and give you
some medicine? they said they wouldn't do

that either / so i convinced them to go nearby to a place

underneath a bridge / not a bridge / you know like an

overpass / underneath the overpass / i met them there with

gauze and antiseptics / i cleaned their wounds and told them

they should really see a doctor / i wrote down my telephone

number and said *if you don't go to a doctor and it gets*

worse give me a call / i told the woman *if he gets a*

headache or something make sure and get some help

because it could be very dangerous / later that morning

i received a call from the woman at home / telling me in

broken english that the man was feeling nauseous

i suspected brain trauma / i met them in order to take him

to the hospital / but he refused / he wouldn't

come with me / i said *look* / *this is very dangerous* / *you*

might die / **NO WAY** he said / **NO WAY** / **NO**

HOSPITAL / **NO WAY** / so i did what i could / i tried to

relieve his pain by laying him out flat on a piece of wood / i

applied water compresses / i did what i could do / if it was

hemorrhaging then the man would die / but if it was just

swelling of the nerves in the brain tissue / then the cold

compresses and the laying flat would help / i left them / to

this day i don't know what happened to that couple / but a

week later i received a phone call from an old woman / she

it's over

could barely speak english / she said **SOMEBODY GIVE THIS NUMBER ME** / **NEED HELP** / **PLEASE COME PLEASE** / when i met her i discovered a really bad infection in her mouth / i said *let's go to the hospital* / she said **NO HOSPITAL** / **NO HOSPITAL!** i thought well / maybe this is a normal reaction of old people / poor people or immigrants / hispanics / whatever it was / these were people who were scared of hospitals and doctors / and after all could i blame them? i'd seen plenty of excellent reasons for being scared of hospitals and doctors

little by little i got more and more phone calls from people that i didn't know / old women / single mothers / teenagers all people who could barely speak a word of english / all people who refused to go to the hospital / most of them spoke spanish / they were either from cuba / el salvador / nicaragua or mexico / all i knew was they were all most likely illegal aliens / petrified of getting caught by some authority and sent back to their country / sent back to i don't know what death / poverty / civil war / it never dawned on me that some of them were dealing in drugs / i was very naive i didn't know a thing about that world

rhona knew what i was doing and she didn't like it she made it clear that she didn't approve / but she was crazy about me and just pretended she didn't know where i was going / she pretended she didn't hear the phone calls (even when she took the messages herself) it was a little game we played / we were living this sort of fairly normal life where she was a nurse and i was a medical student who studied all the time / and i just had this little charity work or something on the side that we never talked about / like a married couple where one is a democrat and the other is a staunch republican / you just don't talk about certain things with each other after about two months the situation started getting out of control / somehow my number got out to a whole network of families / all people with no medical care whatsoever / not just medical care / they wouldn't go near any person in a uniform or any professional of any kind / i got the impression that some of these people never even went outside during the day / i was going to addresses in areas of the city i never even knew existed / i remember i told a friend that i was on such and such a street / he looked at me with his mouth all open and said **you must be nuts!** that is the most **dangerous cutthroat war zone in the whole county** / i would go there and people would see me and say **doctor doctor** / i told them *i'm not a doctor / don't call me that* / they'd say **yes doctor** / nobody would touch me if it was dangerous in the places i went i was immune to it one time i saw a group of guys (probably a gang) walking towards me / i got scared because they looked pretty threatening / but then one guy said **oh** / **he's okay he's the doctor** / **don't touch this guy**

i began to take little things from the hospital like zinc sulfate because this old man poured spaghetti on his feet and the boiling water burned the skin off of all his toes / with my help he recovered beautifully / another time i took some antibiotics to help a few people with really bad bronchitis eventually i borrowed items from the hospital on a fairly regular basis in order to have a ready supply of penicillin gauze / different kinds of analgesics / things like that mostly i was administering basic first aid to these people elementary stuff / they needed help and i was the only one they would see to get it / i guess i was blind to anything else that might have been going on / all i saw was people in need of care / i didn't ask them what they did with their time all i asked was that they never give me anything in exchange

it's over

i refused their money / i refused their gifts (they always tried to give me things) **i wouldn't even take a piece of toast from them** / i knew that i was breaking the rules / if not the law / i knew that i was taking a risk / but i also knew that i was helping people who were sick / in my heart of hearts i felt certain that i was doing the right thing / the ethical thing / i figured as long as i wasn't profiting in any way / i was on pretty solid ground / in a month or two i'd be taking my boards and then i'd be off somewhere to do my residency / no harm done / so a few illegal aliens are a little healthier than if i hadn't existed

what's the big deal?

but then one day the understanding was broken / there was a knock on my door / i opened it and nobody was there except for a brown paper bag on the floor / inside the bag was a big white rock the size of a soccer ball / **a huge white rock** / rhona wasn't home thank god / i looked at this thing and i knew what it was / but i couldn't believe it i knocked on the door of my next-door neighbor the lawyer i showed it to him / he nearly fell to the ground / he said **my god** / **this is like five thousand dollars worth of cocaine you got** he asked me for a piece / i said to him *look* / *i know you're a cocaine addict* / *okay* / *i'll give you a little piece* / *but that's it* / *i'm going to get rid of this thing* / he begged me to give it to him / i said *if i give this to you you'd probably be dead by the morning* / *because i know you'll take it all at once and then you'll die on me* / *and i don't want to be responsible* / *besides you're the only lawyer i know* / i cut him a little piece then went back to my apartment / locked the door / put the white rock on a glass table in the living room got a knife from the kitchen / and steadied my shaking hands (i was so nervous) as i cut the thing into four pieces / then i put all of it in a tray / went to the bathroom and one chunk at a time / flushed the whole thing down the toilet / as i watched each quadrant dissolve into the toilet water and then disappear forever down the drain / i thought about the amount of money my neighbor spends on cocaine every month / i knew that if someone wanted to they could have made a lot of money with this thing / they could have mixed it with some powder and sold it for **ten thousand dollars** because it was pure cocaine / i thought of several people who'd have me committed for flushing something that valuable down the toilet / but there it went

one / two / three / four

gone

i went into the kitchen and washed the knife and tray i scrubbed and scrubbed and scrubbed / i was so upset / to me it was like someone left a bomb outside my door / i was furious with whoever brought this to me / i wanted to find the person and scream *i told you never to give me anything anything!* but i had no idea who sent it to me / eventually i realized that this gift wasn't just from one person / this was a community getting together and deciding to give me something / they knew i wouldn't take any money / so they gave me something they had access to / the next time i got a call / i told them *it's over / no more doctor! don't call me anymore / go to a hospital / go to a real doctor / don't bother me anymore!* but it just so happened that a man was dying of a bullet wound i screamed for them to call an ambulance / but they just said **NO HOSPITAL NO HOSPITAL** / so i went one last time / a bullet was lodged very close to this man's femur / it was right next to his ass / he was in terrible pain / he'd lost a lot of blood / he was in sepsis / his whole system was poisoned

it's over

his skin was blue / his lips were white / he couldn't talk
his eyes were completely lost / his pupils were dilated (which
is a sign of being very close to death) i absolutely insisted they
take the guy to the hospital / i screamed / i yelled / i didn't
want to do anything / i said *this guy's gonna die
comprende? comprende? he's dying
nada nada / esto no más / emergency
emergency / you people are crazy! you
have to take him to the hospital!*
then i left / i refused to help him

when i got home i received another phone call / i said
*forget about it / this is too serious for me to do
alone* / they called again / they said **man in bad shape
very bad very very bad** / **you must come** / **you
have to come** / they were crying / i'm hearing all kinds
of noises over the phone / screaming and wailing / your
heart breaks when you hear that / believe me / i had no
choice / i had to go / i thought i was finished
with these people / i was trying to study / i was trying to get
on with my life / my brain felt like it was being smashed inside
a steel box whose walls were closing in on me / one wall was
what was right / another was *what was legal* / another *what
was safe* / and the last wall was *what had to be done*

i took a taxi / i asked his people to take him by force into the
taxi / i pleaded with them / but nobody would do it / there
was nothing / nothing i could do at this point but try to save
the man's life / i knew i couldn't do it alone / there was no
way i could retrieve the bullet by myself / i had to make sure
that the guy didn't bleed more than was necessary / i needed
assistance next to me to keep cleaning the wound while i'm
doing the surgery / so i called rhona to come and help me out
i said *look i'm doing something here / it's illegal but i
have no choice / i have to do it / a man could be dying*

and they won't let me take him to the hospital / i have
to do this and i need your help / i asked her to drop by
the hospital to get me some gauze / some surgical gloves
antiseptics and some molasses to stop the coagulation / i sent
the cab back to pick her up / two hours later she arrived / i
gave the man a very high dose of penicillin / then proceeded
with the surgery / i opened him up with a kitchen knife which
i sterilized / the wound wasn't difficult to open / everything
was so rotten i could have done it with my hand for god's sake
i opened the wound / i cleaned it with soap and water / i
retrieved the bullet with as much care as i could / it was a
big messy shit / i mean how could i make a mistake? the
guy was dying anyway / so why
should i be afraid? that's what gave me the
courage / i knew no matter what i did / he couldn't
get any worse / he could only get better

the operation was a complete success / the man broke into
a fever but never fell into a coma / the bullet was removed
the wound cleaned and sewn back up / three weeks later he
was walking around / he thanked me / he thanked me so
much / it was a pleasure to see / truly / it's a delightful
experience to see a man on the edge of death come back to
life and thank you for your services / can you think of
something more rewarding than that?

rhona didn't fight me on this / she did just what i said / she
knew that i wasn't a doctor and that she shouldn't be helping
me / she knew it was against the law for her to administer an
intravenous without the okay of a doctor / she probably
violated every code in the book / but she did what i asked her
to do and i appreciated that / my fatal mistake was three
weeks later leaving the stocking of another woman in her bed

what a sloppy asshole i am!

it's over

apparently / the morning after she found the stocking rhona went to the medical school and snitched on me / to this day i don't know exactly what she told them / but she told them something / i was eating lunch at the hospital cafeteria and two security guards came up to my table and asked me if i'm claude debs / i said *yes* / would you please come with us sir / they wouldn't tell me what was going on they had me fill out some forms / then told me i could go when i got home rhona and all her things were gone / two days later i received a notice to show up at the university court for a hearing / i didn't even know what it was all about / they don't tell you whether you're a witness to something or a suspect or if you just didn't pay a traffic ticket / everything was hush hush for two weeks / i was petrified that rhona found out about the cocaine somehow / i couldn't figure out how she'd know / when i showed up for the preliminary hearing i found out i was suspected of impersonating a doctor it turns out i was under surveillance since the moment rhona snitched on me / they had someone undercover for two weeks following me around trying to catch me at something / they wanted to find out if i received any money / and if i did where i had it hidden / but there was no money to be found / no secret bank accounts / no mattresses stuffed with cash there was nothing! whatever i did i did purely out of humanitarian reasons

what i found out at the preliminary hearing brought my entire world crashing down on me in seconds / a shroud of darkness enveloped everything i had worked for and dreamed of becoming / it turns out they were moving ahead on having me expelled from medical school and disqualified from taking the boards / the possibility of criminal charges was being considered as well / i heard people saying things / dates were being thrown around / allegations were being made / it all seemed like a dream / like a terrible dream to me another date was set for a proceeding / like a trial or a final hearing or whatever it was they were calling it / i don't know what it was because i never showed up / i asked my lawyer friend what he thought i should do / he said **well you can stay here and fight it or you can leave / just leave and never come back** / so i thought real hard i got to thinking maybe i made a few mistakes in judgment one or two mistakes / maybe i was a bit too naive / i looked at myself in the mirror / i looked honestly into my soul (which is a far more demanding standard than a jury of peers) and i was cleared of all wrongdoing / i was completely exonerated of all charges / i wasn't guilty of anything other than being there for my fellow human beings when they cried out for help / if i was guilty of anything it was for having too big a heart in a world full of stupid rules and regulations / so i saved a guy's life who would have died if i turned my back on him

in another world perhaps i would have been held up as a hero! in this world they'd never understand / in this world all they seemed to want to do is nail me to the cross

so i made a quick decision to take it on the chin like a man i took my passport and my wallet / packed a bag of clothes and left / i just left / i left my apartment / i left my furniture and my film equipment and all my videotapes and all my books / i left the medical school and the hope of becoming a great scientist and finding a cure for cancer / i left the city i left the state / i left whatever friends i had made / i left my shame / my embarrassment / i left all regrets / i left my entire past / everything that had come before that moment i left behind / and went out to start a whole new existence

witness

i have very little patience for stupidity

i am always in disagreement

with people around me

if

dissidence

the

was rewarded in this world

at

i would be

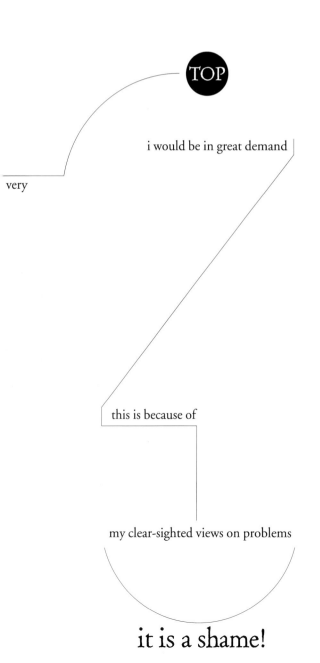

TOP

i would be in great demand

very

this is because of

my clear-sighted views on problems

it is a shame!

the things i come up with

nobody

nobody else could think of

at my age

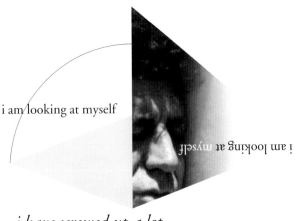

i am looking at myself

i have screwed up a lot

i think i know

what the problem might be

i have an inability to belong

i have a resistance to belonging to anybody

to anyplace   to anything

i strive   to belong

not

to possess

witness

i don't want to belong to

any particular race

any particular religion

i once was an ardent leftist

any particular political party

or nationality

then i went to moscow three times

now i am an anticommunist

i have a fear of belonging

maybe i just can't belong anywhere

i am going to accept this!

i will accept this!

i am going to go through life

never really committing

- to anything

- to anyplace

- to anybody

i have so much to offer

it's a shame / but that's okay / it's okay

i am not particularly spiteful

i am really

i really am!

i have worn many masks in my life

·

i need to experience as much as possible

·

why live the life of one person

·

when you could live the life of twenty?

that is what it is!

happy!

i am constantly trying to

maximize

my contact with life

people can say all kinds of things

anything they want about me

if i see something i want

i will do **anything** i can to get it

i maximize the pleasure by
believing that it's my last chance
to do whatever it is i am doing

i have always

done this!

i am not melancholic

i actually have a very
positive attitude

it's only that i am exasperated

i am extremely satisfied
with myself

exasperated by my
constant failure

i have lived wherever
i wanted to live

my constant failure to lead

i've done whatever i wanted
without hurting a soul

my constant failure to lead
a triumphant and exemplary life

i have not succumbed
to limitations

in a world run by imposters

i do not complain

i often put myself in the
worst possible positions

i have nothing
to complain about

the worst possible positions

i would never exchange
a minute of my life

in the end
if nothing else

i will be able to look at
myself in the mirror and know
that i have *truly truly lived*

one of three things

oh my god / is that blood?

there are bloodstains on my underpants!

there's blood in the toilet

there's blood passing
through my urine
goddamn!

what the?

what is that? pus?

is that pus? it looks like

it looks like tissue or something

like little pieces of tissue from my kidneys

i can't believe this!
it hurts so much

what's going on here?

okay

calm down

just calm down

think this through objectively

look at the facts / if someone else walked

in here with this / what would i do? first thing

i'd do is try to calm them down / calm their nerves

then i'd tell them *i'm sure there's an explanation for*

why it's happening / *let's find out what it is — together*

okay? then we'll try to fix it / it doesn't sound so convincing

when you're the patient / when it's happening to you / okay

snap out of it and think / think! what could this be?

okay / okay / it could be / it could be one of three things:

1

it could be a stone

it could be just a kidney stone

which *could* mean an operation / shit!
there's no way / shit! there's
no way i could have an operation
right now / i can't afford it / not
the money / not the time
not the aggravation

okay

calm down

don't just assume the worst

there doesn't have to be an operation

there's always a chance if it is a stone / it could

just pass through the system / but if it is just a normal

kidney stone / there wouldn't be any pus / which means

if it is a stone / damn it / if i do have stones
then they're probably lodged in a way that
they can't get out / which would definitely
mean an operation / shit!

but the good thing is / i don't have a fever / because if it

was kidney stones / i would have a fever / so that means it's

probably not a stone / it's probably not kidney stones at all

2

the second thing it could be is urethritis

it could be an infection lodged in my kidney from

having anal sex / some piece of shit virus bacteria could have

just crawled up into my bladder / up to the urethra and then

one of three things

into my kidneys and just lodged there

jesus christ!
it could be
just stuck there
wreaking havoc

that would be horrible! so dangerous!

come on now

pull yourself together

be logical for a minute and think! think!

think! if it was the urethra there'd definitely

be a burning sensation in the lymph nodes / but i

don't feel any burning / which makes it

highly unlikely that it is in the urethra

3

so then the third thing it could be

is my prostate / my goddamn prostate

oh god / please let it not be my prostate

because if it is my prostate / it could just be

terribly inflamed or something

but in all likelihood

it's a very bad case of prostatitis

which means it could be

oh man

it could be the beginning
of a cancer
a goddamn
piece of shit
cancer!

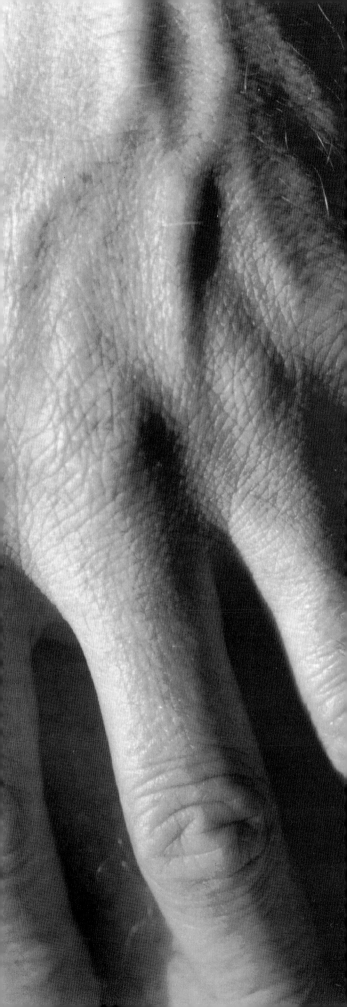

eleanor

what disgusts me most about the whole thing is that she started saying to me that i was her son

and then / only then / after i had grown to see her as my mother / the mother i felt i never really had / the mother i longed for / the mother i had now received somehow somewhere in the middle of my life / like a sweepstakes prize from the lottery of the gods / it was only then / only after she took me into her home when i was sick / and cared for me as a mother takes care of her child / only after eleven months of her maternal nurturing / only after my reciprocating that love by caring for her and looking out for her as if she was my mother it was only after months of my calling her *mother* / and then with her consent *mama* / and her responding **yes my son** *mama mama* / **my son my son** / *mama* / **son** / *mama* **son** / only after all of that was established and in place did she turn around and **assassinate** the trust **violate** the affection and understanding / destroying everything we had between us in an instant

sure i loved her!

i admit it / i always said that i loved her / i loved her as only a son could love his mother / it had nothing to do with her being rich / i loved the idea of her being there for me / i loved that she would cook for me / she'd cook me dinner / she'd make me breakfast / she was a terrible cook / but that wasn't the point / it was the thought that counted / she would cook up these completely awful czechoslovakian and hungarian dinners / **they were horrible** / but it didn't matter / just knowing that she wanted nothing else but to please me / touched me so / she spent hours cooking for me / she did it with love / she'd heat up my plate before serving a hot dish / she would always have freshly washed napkins for every meal / cloth napkins! she created this insulated / comforting environment for me / i felt / i felt i think for the first time in my life / i actually had a feeling of security / i think i actually felt in some way protected by her / by the feeling of home she provided me

so you can imagine what a shock it was the first time it happened / the very first time / i remember / i looked at her and all i could see was the distorted image of a confused and desperate old woman / you see / she had very bad back pains arthritis / plus disk problems / degenerative disk disease / and she had a terrible time falling asleep / so i had no objection to massaging her when she requested it / massaging a mother what could be the harm in massaging your mother? never really having had a mother / i mean *a real* / *a loving* mother i was unfamiliar with the nature of such a relationship / if anything i figured it was the normal thing to do / so i played my role / i was the good son / i put my heart into my fingers and tried my best to massage away her awful pains

she would tell me that anything i wanted could be mine i told her again and again that i wanted nothing for myself i told her that everything she chose to give would go to the foundation / i didn't want a single thing for myself / not a penny / nothing / **nothing!** when we would go out to the theater / i would pay for my own ticket / if it was for the foundation it was okay / i made this absolutely clear / if she gave money / she was giving to a nonprofit foundation that helped the elderly and the destitute / it was a tax-deductible philanthropic thing for her / it was the christian thing to do / she was the patron saint needed to turn a good idea into a reality / believe me / she loved knowing

eleanor

that without her the whole thing would never ever fly / it
boosted her ego let me tell you / our arrangement was
perfectly clear / i was to be the director of programs while she
handled the financial end / it was entirely aboveboard / if we
developed feelings for each other beyond our shared interest
in the foundation they were solely expressed in terms of
mother son / there was nothing that could have been
construed as anything else but that / i was very careful to be
totally clear about what the foundation meant to me
what she meant to me / i created no illusions

i massaged her for several months before i became aware that

anything else was going on / then one time after massaging
her / she asked me to stay in bed with her so she could relax
and get some sleep / i said *well* / *okay* / and reluctantly
crawled underneath the covers / she had these luxurious
billowing blankets / and she always had clean / soft flannel
sheets / and silk pillowcases / i have to admit that for a
moment i languished in the comfort of that bed / it was
very tempting in its own way / very soothing actually / to
be in a bed like that / under the puff of such covers / the
fuzzy touch of sheets like that / and with a mother at my side
it was very tempting in its own way / at the same time i felt
awkward being there / under there with her / although i had
very little to go on / somewhere in the back of my mind i
suspected something could be wrong about this under-the-
covers situation with my newly adopted mother / so i rolled
slowly / ever so slowly i rolled to the other side of the bed
as far as i could go without falling onto the floor / after about
an hour of staring at the wrong side of her bedroom door
after i had inspected every inch of that door / the molding

around the door / the perfect mitering of the molding around
the door / the brass doorknob reflecting the oak dresser / the
shadow cast diagonally across the door onto the wall from the
light above the headboard / after about an hour of us both
lying there in silence on opposite sides of this king-size bed
i got up / walked into the living room / turned on the t.v.
and went to sleep on the sofa

in the morning she came at me like a lion / she was *ferocious*
i'd never seen her like that / she told me that i had deserted her
that i had left her alone when she needed me the most

from that night on / after every massage there would be a
similar scene / except that her insistence and her need for me
increased / till finally one night / i was finishing a bowl of
borscht at the dining room table / we were just about to leave
to go see this delightful little opera called *idomeneo* / do you
know it? / it's one of mozart's obscure gorgeous little operas
it's one of my favorites / anyway / she was in the bathroom
putting on her makeup / going on and on about how i didn't
really care about her / about how i'm using her / taking
advantage of her / all this crap / so i just put my spoon down
stood up / threw my hands into the air / and said

okay eleanor
what is it you really want?
i really don't understand!
you're always upset
i never seem to be able
to please you
what is it that you
really want?

she came into the kitchen and with such vehemence
she slammed this plate of hungarian meat onto the table before

eleanor

me / it was cooked in a kind of a milk sauce / the incredible

force of the impact made the hot milk and bloody juices of the

meat spring up into my face / all over my shirt / and down my

pants / her face was gnarled into a knot whose vortex was a set

of clenched teeth / yet somehow she managed to shout

i want you
to be my
lover

i stood there in disbelief / staring at her / dumbfounded

after a while i regained my breath and said *no way*
not in a million years
are you crazy?

well / after i said that / she just exploded

she slashed me with her tongue

with her poisonous tongue / **she slashed me!**

it was so ugly / it was so pathetic and ugly / *accchhhh* / how

could she? how could she have done that? how could she have

done that to me? to us? to what we had together? i mean come

on / i'm no dummy / by that time i had read the writing on

the wall / i *knew* she was lonely / it's not that i think that

there's anything wrong with her desiring a man half her age

and it's not that i think that it's impossible or even all that

unreasonable for me to be with a seventy-five-year-old woman

in that way / i was with an old lady once / i was in my twenties

and she was eighty something / she wanted it and i was able to

satisfy her / plus it was a curiosity to me / but with eleanor

it was a completely different framework / can you understand

that in my mind she *was* my mother / and that the idea of

having sex with my mother was **utterly revolting!**

it felt like i was being boiled and skinned alive! can you see the predicament i was in? not only was i sick / i had no home to go to / i was penniless / my life had lost direction / i was nowhere without her help / and she knew it / my god / she had me right where she wanted me / she knew that she could completely pulverize me! she knew that she could crush me she knew it! and do you know what she did?

she actually tried to crush me!

three months had passed since that first incident in her bed three exhausting months of deflecting her nightly reproaches pacifying lust with affection / three months during which my own health deteriorated to the point where i was helpless and almost completely dependent on her care / there i was / stuck inside her park avenue apartment running a fever of a hundred and four degrees / i swear to you i thought i was going to die even though i had a preexisting condition / she managed to get me a health insurance policy / she drove me to the doctor she came with me into the doctor's office like a parent comes along with her young child / she paid for the medication i was grateful for her concern / i thanked her profusely then she'd insist i sleep in her bed / i always said

no!

i was burning up / there were clumps of blood in my urine / my kidneys were deteriorating / my liver was barely functioning / the idiotic doctors with all their tests and fancy equipment couldn't figure out what the hell was wrong with me i couldn't move / i tell you i could not move / i was stuck there in her living room / the sicker i got the more she insisted i sleep in her bed / **you must sleep here claude / how can i take care of you if you're all the way out there in the living room? you must claude! you must!**

eleanor

i refused / but she wouldn't let up / then one night i was

asleep on the sofa / she came and woke me and insisted

i come into her room and sleep in her bed / i unequivocally

refused to do so / i said *no thank you*

the sofa is just fine thank you

she said **you must sleep in the bed**

you can't sleep on the sofa

that's no place to sleep when

you're sick / you're sick

claude / you're sick!

i said *fine / you don't want me to sleep on*

the sofa / i will sleep on the floor!

i rolled down onto the floor taking the blankets and her

precious hot-water bottle with me / using one of my beat-up

old shoes for a pillow / for a few moments i actually fell back

asleep on the floor! that enraged her so / she ran towards me

and started kicking me with such anger / she kicked

me and kicked me and kicked me / she

kicked me right in my liver / she kicked right

where she knew it would hurt the most / she kicked me her

lethal kicks / and believe me she knew where to kick / she saw

the x-rays / she sent in the insurance forms / she witnessed

me writhing in pain / she knew where it hurt and she went for

it with the jagged ends of her venomous overgrown toenails

my gut – the bull's-eye of her rage

doubled over / wriggling on the floor like a captured dying

rat / i looked up from her plush beige carpet with my feverish

bleary eyes / i looked up at her and i saw cruelty like i had

never seen before / i saw this woman / i saw my newfound

mother turn into a vampire / a mutual friend of ours had

warned me (he was no sweetheart himself / so i didn't take

him seriously) he told me **beware of her now / she's**

been rejected by you / she will destroy you!

did i listen to him? no / i gave her the benefit of the doubt

even though by that point i didn't really have very much choice
i knew what had to be done / i tore up the insurance policy
and the insurance card she got me / then i gathered up the
few things i was able to carry: a toothbrush / a coat
some underwear / and a few pictures

while she was in the kitchen screaming at the pots and pans
i quietly closed the door behind me / limped down six double
flights of stairs / wobbled past the doorman / my hot flesh
plunged into the cold wet air of the city / into the pouring
rain / with neither a penny in my pocket
nor a home to go to

beck and call

warren

warren

warren

are you there warren? where the hell are you?

you told me you'd be gone for one day / maybe you said

the weekend / okay / but this is four / five days now

where on earth are you? you're never

home / i call you and all i get is this stinking machine / i

know / i know you're getting to be some kind of a hotshot

now / speaking here / going there / doing this and that

i understand that / and i'm happy for you / believe me

i couldn't be happier for your little successes / the little

triumphs you're having with your little career you got going

there / i think it's great / it's terrific!

and this new woman you met / i couldn't be happier for you

but you know / you're not the only one in the world my

friend / as much as you like to cherish your *independence*

as much as you treasure your *self-sufficiency* / just remember

that you didn't get there all by your lonesome / you've always

managed to surround yourself with people who allow you your

self-indulgences / people who support your idiosyncratic

dabblings / nurture your fantasies / and hold your sweaty

hand through your many childish delusional attacks of fear

look / all i am trying to say is / all i'm asking is that

you consider for a moment / just a moment / maybe take

a second out of your all-important life / and consider that

there are other people in the world who
might actually have needs / who might need a

place to stay (for instance) or who might just want to talk to you or see you / there might even be one or two people from your past who need your help / someone who shouldn't have to even ask you for it / someone who always dropped whatever it was he was doing / no matter how busy he was at the time / just to help you / whenever there was the slightest tremor of a need in your voice / he was there someone who drove over sixty miles once / in the middle of the night in order to comfort you when you were sick remember that? no matter how psychosomatic the illness might have been / there were no questions asked / never any questions asked / he was there for you when others deserted you / he was there picking you up off the ground / cheering you on / tending your wounds / do you remember how many times he was there for you? folding five thousand mailers and stuffing them into envelopes / loading and hauling cartons and cases of your all-too-weighty projects / driving the truck / sweeping the floor / patching the holes in the walls / he was there helping! but where are you now / when he (who has always been so devoted and selfless) is asking for your help or just a little of your attention / where the goddamn hell on earth are you?

love message

i know you're out there

having some sort of a **great time**

i know you're out on the town / you're having a good ol'

good ol' time / i know where you are / i know who you're

with / you're out there somewhere / you're at some club with

your so-called *girlfriend* / maybe you're with a whole group

of friends / a whole mob of your artist comrades / on a big

night out on the town / another night in the bowels of some

downtown scene / i can hear the frivolous banter / i can hear

it / you're probably at some smoke-filled jazz club / pressing

your chapped lips against your fourth bottle of beer / dark

beer / imported from germany / bottled in new jersey / i

know / i know where you are / i know what you're doing

you've got your shoes off / you're smelling up the whole place

with your stinking feet / you're probably sitting there with

your eyes closed / **bopping** / that's what you call it

right? **bopping** / bopping your skinny ass to that

vulgar music / *boinga boinga boinga* / that

music i'll never understand / nor care to / i know you're out

there / and you won't make it home till two or three in the

morning / many beers later / after hours and hours of those

hideous screeching sounds / pushing their way

through your waxy ears / *eccchhhh!*

i know you / don't you think i know you by now?

i know where you are / i know you're with your girl / her

soft hand cupped adoringly into your arm / you: so

self-consumed / too busy thinking about the whole cosmos

to notice anything but yourself / she: just wanting you

to be happy / wanting to make you happy / *just you*

wanting to be / needing to be needed / feeling needed
totally needed / by you / i know / i know what goes on

i know where you are / i know where you both are / i can see
you drowning out the incessant chatter of your own thoughts
wasting the precious moments of your life / *letting your hair
down* / convincing yourself that you're entitled / you're
entitled to spend a little money / you're entitled to bathe in
the night of jungle rhythms / pretending you're the first man
on earth / pretending you're in your cave with your savage
woman / pretending you're in outer space en route to
unknown galaxies / floating weightlessly on a cloud
of the sonic nothingness that surrounds you

but who am i to say? who am i to say
anything? i wouldn't say anything
i'm not going to say anything
because who am i to question what you do / who you
do it with / how you spend your time / your money / what
you choose to do or don't do with your talent / i'm not gonna
play that role with you / i've got better things to do than think
about how you waste your life away / you wouldn't listen to
me anyway / go ahead! you deserve it / you do!
you've earned the right to piss your time into nightclubs of
forgetfulness / have fun! go out / go out
there and be *entertained!* i don't care if you never come home
i suppose i should just be thankful that you let me have this
room in your basement / it would be too much to ask to
actually see you from time to time / i wouldn't want to cramp
your social life / go out there / night after night / have your
fun / enjoy yourself / while i'm downstairs working / twenty
hours a day / seven days a week / in terrible pain / i'm in
terrible pain! but i don't complain / if i knew
i could live forever / as you seem to know your fate / then
perhaps i could join you in your fun / in your party time / in

love message

your *tax-deductible cultural research* / have some fun / kill some time / but even then / **even then** / i doubt it i doubt i would join you / because there's always (if you never allow yourself to become satisfied) there is always work to be done / **the work is never done** / not for the night / not for your life / don't forget what i told you: they buried beethoven with his hands clenched into fists he died screaming **not yet! not**

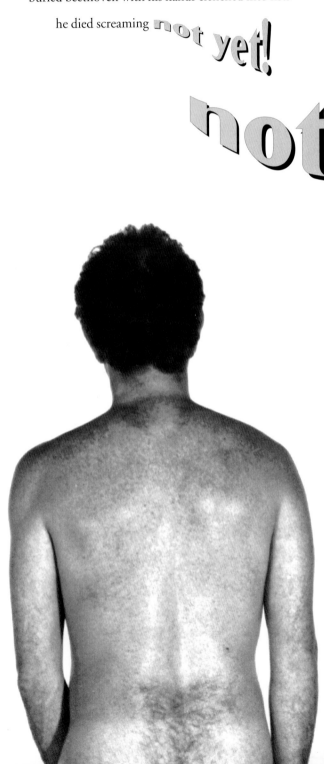

listen / i have to go / i have a million and one things
that need my attention / i have an investor who's interested
in the magazine / i have to get everything ready for a big
presentation with him on monday / there's a large import
company interested in that other project i was telling you
about / i'm swamped! oh / and uh / listen / don't worry
about the help you promised to give me / i can manage the
whole thing on my own / even though i can hardly walk at
this point / i'll be okay / as long as you had a wonderful time
tonight / that's all that really matters / really! i don't know
if you were thinking about me (i doubt it) but you know
you're always in my thoughts / because you know how much
i love you **no matter what!** even if you never
come back to this big empty house of yours / even if i never
ever see you again / i'll always love you / alright then
good night / good night sweetheart / and kiss
your girlfriend good night for me too

farewell

we are growing older you and i

we will change less and less with each passing year

your selfishness will only harden with time / my needs will

only increase more and more as the days go by / yes you gave

me a place to stay / but i need more from you than that / i

shouldn't have to tell you what i need / i shouldn't have to

teach you how to be a best friend / that is why it's time to turn

the page on our friendship before it completely deteriorates

my hands are trembling / my eyes are red with tears / it is

very very hard to bid farewell / **but i must / we**

must! call me melodramatic / call me hysterical / tell

me that i'm overreacting / dismiss me as acting like a child

do as you wish / think what you need to think / i am on my

hands and knees – *crying* / our friendship has suffered a fatal

shipwreck / we both can no longer change

(we will not have to)

be happy my dear friend (you and your girlfriend)

work hard / and have lots of love and a long long life / that's

what i wish for you / we must have the courage to resist seeing

each other / instead of looking towards a future filled with

petty wrangling and unmet expectations / let's just cherish the

memories / the magic moments we've had together: getting

ourselves thrown out of the mandarin restaurant (laughing

hysterically all the way home) playing the granite walls of the

beinecke library like a drum in an echo chamber / staying up

all night / so many nights talking soul to soul in the dark

that time when you and jan and i camped in the rain on mount

greylock and suddenly you undressed and we all danced naked

around the fire / **i fell in love with you**

that night / i swear i felt you **in my bones** / the many times we played music together / me on the mandolin / you on anything in sight (pots and pans / the floor / a pair of spoons) the day we walked forever on hammonasset beach and that school of shimmering fish leaped above the waves / the two fishermen we saw and you turned to me and said **maybe they're so close they don't have to talk** / the two lovers we saw at the indian restaurant staring into each other's eyes / holding hands and i turned to you and said *they'll never last* (and we thought for sure they heard me) you reading me henry miller and gertrude stein / me reading goethe and rilke / the balloon that froze then exploded / leaving its form in the ice on the deck in new fairfield / the scarlet tree / the osprey / the night we heard a raccoon devouring a cat / all the japanese films we saw together *do des ka den* / *woman in the dunes* / our ménage à trois with katharine / our ménage à trois with the manic depressive (who i almost married) our ménage à trois with the hippie (they all said that you were a better lover / they all said that you kissed them and held them with such tenderness and love / yet i was never jealous) the day we discovered the field of red and pink roses / **those are the times we must keep etched in our hearts!** okay? let's not destroy it with the prolonged agony of a rotting friendship / **we must stop it now** / before the putrid odor of decay clogs these wonderful memories / of course i was very tempted to read your letter and take down your new address / but i didn't for both of us / i didn't / warren / you will always be my eyes / my windows to the world / please understand / my last words to you my friend are words of love / to both you and your girlfriend / farewell / may it rain on sundays evermore!

snapshot

a woman is asleep on the ground
pigeons circle around her

rummaging through the filthy debris
there is another figure / an older woman / also
asleep / she is in blue jeans / i am looking at her
ass / it's too skinny for me / i move on

over there i see an old couple

a man and a woman / they are holding each other / wrapped
together in a bundle / they are as old as stones / sleeping
shoulder to shoulder / this man and this woman comfort each
other here in the frost of winter / perhaps they have comforted
each other through the frigid hardships of a lifetime / they
are lucky to get such a good spot for the night / they are lucky
to get some sleep on this painfully uncomfortable / hard
splintered bench / they have nothing / except newspapers and
bags / bags and bags filled with newspapers / old newspapers
so old they are all mostly yellow / why do they carry this
collection of newspapers? they have kitchen utensils / plastic
forks and knives / everything is plastic! plastic
cups / plastic bags / there are plastic bags with nothing inside
but other plastic bags / plastic bags with clothing / but mostly
plastic bags with newspapers / they are very fond of plastic bags
they are very fond of old newspapers / their life is structured
around plastic bags / plastic bags are very important to them

they smell / these two people / and i am very much like
them / i know that i am beginning to stink myself / i can
smell their odor from where i stand / it's very striking / it is
a putrid odor / it gets into the pores of your nose and it stays
there / you can taste it in your mouth / it's difficult to get
rid of / they carry that odor with their bags / they carry it
everywhere they go / this old couple / they are in the most
uncomfortable position / and yet they look as
peaceful as two babies in a crib

self-respect is lost / integrity is very hard to find

they have come to this earth (both of them) have come to this
planet / and now they are old / they have so little to enjoy
a universe / limited to an old blanket / a cup of coffee
perhaps chicken broth / and maybe / maybe
a bottle of cheap wine from time to time

some place to stay

i figured if i'm going to get murdered / i'd rather get murdered indoors than out on the street / so i looked for places to sleep where it's dark and a little bit warm / you know the only theaters that stay open all night are porno theaters

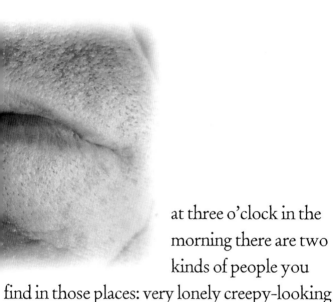

at three o'clock in the morning there are two kinds of people you find in those places: very lonely creepy-looking perverts and those who just need a place to stay / if you pay $1.25 you can spend the night they're **disgusting filthy environments** / roaches all over the place / rats climbing up the walls / but you can crawl into a seat in the corner and get a couple of hours sleep and it's relatively safe because why would a mugger pay $1.25 to mug you / when they can do it outside for free?

bottom

down here

i'm down here!

i'm all the way down here

come on ... further

i'm all the

..further...come on further

further down than that

way down...

all the way down at
the bottom

watch your step / watch your step / it's dangerous down

here / i mean / after a while you get used to it / you'll be

surprised / you'll be surprised how much you can see / after

i give this whole thing some time to blow over / i'm getting

bottom

out of here / what am i to them? **they've got real criminals to chase** / i didn't do anything wrong all i did was try to help some people / **hang me** / **go ahead** / **nail me to the cross!** just because she found a stocking / someone else's stocking in the bed

she had to snitch on me?

be careful / you really have to watch your step / you never know what you're stepping on down here / i never took that job you know / i'd rather be here / i'd never take a job like that / they wanted me though / they knew i was a clever guy they offered me top dollar / six figures / that's all i wanted to know / i just wanted to know if they were smart enough to know how good i was / i knew i'd never take that job / **i**

swore i'd never take a job like that

i'll never work for anybody / i'm my own boss / i'm my own slave driver / i have plans for getting out of here / that's the only way out you know / you need a good idea / and then you need a plan to make it happen / you don't need anything else / don't need a family name / don't need an inheritance don't need to win *the lottery* / don't need a loan or a grant (if i had one i'd give it away) i'd rather start with nothing just an idea / a good idea / a few good ideas / some plans to make it happen / nothing else / a little luck i guess wouldn't hurt / to stop the bleeding / just to stop the bleeding already! there's something wrong with my kidneys / there's blood in my urine / blood in my intestines / it shouldn't be / you know they wanted to operate / they wanted to give me a couple of operations / **i don't have the time for that** / **forget about the money** / **they don't know what they're doing** / **maybe it's this** / **maybe it's that**

they open you up / they look around / they see what's in there / they don't know what they're looking for / i told the doctor *i know my medicine* / *so don't jerk me around* / he tried to jerk me around / i pulled out the catheter myself / i told him he could go to hell! you've got to be wide awake down here / eyes behind your head / leery of every step / careful where you sleep / but you know / for right now / i'd rather start from zero / i'd rather live down here like this / out of sight / make time my doctor / be my own man / i'd rather do this than suck the cock of compromise / i'd rather have it this way live down here / be down here

for now

womb envy

if i could

if there was such a thing as divine intervention

if through some miracle / some mutation of anatomy and

gender / or some advance in reproductive technology

i could actually give birth to a baby / from my

own belly! my own child / my own little bubby

baby oochie coochie huggy honey lovey wovey tushy wooshy

little baby / from my own womb
from my very own tummy

a baby i could feed from my own breast / a

baby i could suckle with my own nourishing

oversensitive nipples / then and only then

would i (without any doubt) i would i would

i would i would i would i would

have my own child

without hesitation or doubt / without delay

i'd have to excuse myself right now and

get to working on it / right away

but / it's not the same for a man / you see / a man's life

is a continuous trajectory / an arrow of will / unbroken by

cycles of periodic bloodletting / except / except of course for

war / which is a process of *destruction* / a man's life can never

be interrupted by the exclamatory punctuations of giving birth

a man's life will never be catapulted by the miracle of creation

my ticket as a man / my ticket at best is to a grandstand seat

in the arena of life's cycles: birth and procreation

that's why i don't want to have any

children! as a man / it's not the same as it is for a

woman / as a man / i can't make a baby / i can't have

a kid / a real kid of my own / from my own loins / a child
that i have to *scream* out of me / a child that i have to *bleed*
to its birth / contract and convulse / sweat / wrench and
twist to life / after months and months of interminable nausea
and inner rumblings / hot to cold / irrational cravings
i would long for that euphoric
suffering / that terrible bliss of life giving / that
abandoned / tearful / screeching / laughter / that
involuntary spasm after spasm / giving birth to breath
giving birth to a crying / bloody / wet / spectacle of life
created out of my own flesh and blood / the two of us

oh!
the two of us
such an unbelievable connection between two bodies
imagine – a man and his baby / umbilically intertwined
which (if it were to happen) nobody / nobody else would
sever but me / i would have to be the one / i would insist on
being the one to cut the cord and liberate that child / set free
that bloody bundle of tender flesh and veins / i'd shield him
(or her) it doesn't make a difference to me / a boy / a girl
either way / i'd shield that baby for an eternal moment in my
arms / for that one moment / i'd shield it from the salivating
panting world that lay outside my paternal arms / that
thankless greedy monster world awaiting another innocent
to spoil / i'd cradle my beautiful / handsome baby / and
nothing (for that precious moment) **nothing** would
penetrate the softness of my hairy fatherly nest

if i could give birth to my own child / i'd make sure it would
be the handsomest / genius baby boy or girl you've ever seen
through my tireless efforts: traveling / doing research and

womb envy

extensive interviews / i'd be able to select the most brilliant
(nobel prize caliber) / earth shakingly good-looking / healthy
mother needed to fertilize my alchemical egg / then i'd
research the latest methods in genetic manipulation / no
matter the cost / i would be prepared to invest whatever
savings i had into adding or restructuring the genes in order
to equip this child with the best ingredients a person could
ever dream of starting out with / i'd also use nontraditional
techniques / hormonal stimulation through nutrition
vitamin supplementation and climate control / and just the
right amount of exercise / i would do whatever i could / my
very best in making sure that i would procreate / not a short
ugly / freckly / pale / combative / sickly odd-ball-in-
the-crowd kind of person like myself / but a well-adjusted
perfectly formed / brilliant / tall / giant of a man / okay
perhaps (in all honesty) i would prefer a boy / so as to ensure
the passing of the torch to one who could in turn
give birth to another luminous creature

of course i'd nurture the child with love and affection as any
parent would / and do my best to insulate him from the harsh
realities of an unfriendly / sick world / then after a certain
age it would be important to expose the child to some quasi-
devastating experiences / look at me! i've had to
endure some of the most horrible abuses and traumas in life
and i am a man of character / a little adversity toughens the
skin / in the long run it might be the best kind of endurance
training a person could have / naturally i would shower my
kid with love / but mostly i would work on developing his
brain / at an early age i would bombard him with music
literature / language / and art / constantly constantly
constantly / i'd bathe him in science / mathematics
and history / i know / i can hear some people saying
be careful / *be careful not to push too much*
it's not natural / *it's not natural* / i hate that

whole concept of *natural* / *what is natural?* i don't think

most people realize what the human brain is capable of / what

a child is capable of achieving / i'd never send my kid to school

i'd do it all myself / what takes the school system

eight years to teach / i could do in two / and then at thirteen

years old / the kid's out of the house just like me / only unlike

me / he will leave with the blessing of his father / and then

he's on his own / equipped / prepared

armored for greatness

hopefully he would grow up to be the kind of man who

wouldn't need to lead other men in disgusting displays of

bravado in order to show his greatness / my child / with any

luck would become the sort of man who will dedicate his life

to creating life / dedicate his life to giving breath to the as-yet

unborn / out of love he would give birth to countless children

and raise them all with an unswerving selflessness / that man

of mine will have a pure / humble nature / with no need to

boast or prove himself to anyone / for to have the gift of

giving life would be all a truly great man could ask for

single room occupancy

they call it a welfare hotel / they call it an s.r.o.

to me it's a shining palace

the bed is a king's womb / the window opens up to the whole

world / at last i have a place i can call my home / i have a

pillow / a door with a lock / a mirror up on the wall / after

months of sleeping in theaters and on park benches / i have

an address / a set of numbers i can call my own

i have a home

i exist

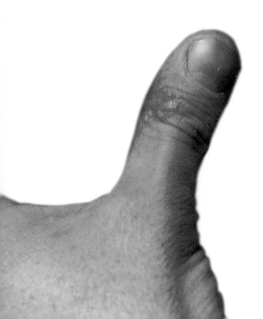

the rules of the game

i always made it very very clear

straight from the beginning / right from the start

there will be no marriages / no marriages! that's what i said to every woman since

marizette and my slavic escapades / i gave up on the whole

idea of marriage / *you want to be together* / *we can have a good*

time / *if it gets to the point where we want to move in with each*

other / *that's great* / *but there will be no marriages* / it was

always very clear / but then the relationship grows / and just

as soon as the patterns of cohabitation take form *the M word*

starts creeping into the conversation / things like **oh you**

would make such a great father / or **do you think**

one day / **if we ever get married we could live**

in paris for a while? until lo and behold she

insists upon it! they all insisted upon it / every

woman i went out with over those seven or eight years always

ended up saying things like **well claude** / **are you**

serious about us or not? followed by the ultimatums

all along i'm thinking we had an understanding / all along

she's living on hope / without saying a word / hoping that

i will change my mind and want to get married

i swore that i would never get married again / i swore that

there would never be anyone who could ever replace marizette

so you can imagine when the day came that i met a woman

a woman who didn't care whether i lived or died / you can

imagine how i felt when all i could think about was getting

married / *will she ever marry me? will i get the chance to grow*

old with her? will she ever talk to me? it was like a volcano

erupted inside my heart / inside my brain

i thought i was going insane!

the first time i noticed her i nearly fell over / i was in the lobby

of the resident hotel (where i was staying) on the upper west

side of manhattan / when she whisked past me through the

front door and out onto the street / i followed her out / but

she was gone / *poof* / she just vanished / like a mirage or

spirit from another dimension / mesmerized by the way

she moved and the confident / knowing look in her eyes

i waited three / four / maybe five hours until she reappeared

she wasn't a mirage! the eighth natural wonder

of the world was staying in my own hotel! she may have been

small in height and weight / but i could tell this was a woman

bound for greatness / i longed for her to go there with me

wherever it was she was going / i didn't fantasize having sex

with her as much as i did being old with her / growing old

with her / this woman captured my entire imagination / yet

as far as she was concerned / i didn't even exist! whenever

she saw me coming she'd look right past my smiles

and advances and nods

it was a very weird feeling / this feeling / i caught the thing

so bad / i caught the thing that infects the songs on the radio

that all-consuming condition that spreads and spreads and

spreads / eating away at the minds of once-great poets and

musicians / reducing them to driveling fools of rhyme and

hackneyed melody / **my god!** within a week i

had become a card-carrying member of the googly-eyed clan of

love-struck zombies / blind / yet full of vision / hypnotized

by the glare of their own mortal hype / i was one of them now

in love / totally one thousand percent head over heels in love

and there was nothing i could do about it

but play the part

good advice

the truth is just one of many many options

take my advice:

lie

you've got to

lie

to maintain your relationships

you've got to tell yourself you're happy just to stay alive

i lie to my wife / i lie to my landlord / i lie to my best friend

my doctor / i'm lying to you right now

but most importantly

i lie to myself!

it's helpful to understand the biochemical origins of

happiness / you see / happiness is relative to the amount of

endorphins secreted by the blood into the brain / people in a

state of love secrete an above-average amount of endorphins

that's why they feel so light / they feel so happy / like they can

just fly away / so all you need to do (on a daily basis) to make

yourself feel happy is **force yourself** to secrete more

endorphins / this can be achieved (i have discovered)

by using an extremely powerful narcotic called

the lie

most people think lies are negative harmful things / but

if you use lies with an understanding of organic medicine

if you use lying as a narcotic / then the lie can be a very strong

positive force / there are negative lies / and there are positive

lies / most people only think of lies in the negative sense

look / i am a very honest man / but i will **lie through my teeth** in order to create a sense of well-being for myself and the people around me / it's not because i'm unhappy / not at all / at this point in my life i'm essentially i'm . . . i'm . . . i'm *very happy* / which might be a lie and it might not / the thing is / by creating the illusion in my brain that i'm in a constant state of quote *love* / that i'm in *love* with my work / in *love* with my friends / my wife / if i tell myself that i'm important / that my life has meaning / and the work that i do is not only valid but essential / if i make the people who work for me / the people around me / believe that they are valuable and important and loved / it keeps them happy it keeps me happy / it keeps everything afloat / if you and i have the illusion that anything you or i might say or do or make **really amounts to a goddamn bit of difference** / then we've got it made!

this approach is in diametric opposition to realists who shoot themselves in the head or drink themselves into oblivion alcohol is a way of getting a lot of quick endorphins into the brain / unfortunately for alcoholics the alcohol dismantles the body's own ability to produce endorphins / that's why when they go in to detox for three days they suffer delirium tremens you have to tie them down to the bed until the body starts producing its own endorphins / it's hell / it's absolute hell for these people / drug addicts who use cocaine or heroin destroy themselves / and spend all their money in the process whereas *lying* as a narcotic is absolutely free! and if used without abuse / can offer many years of continued happiness / if not success!

this whole week / i've been craving *impossible women* / just the idea / the idea of attracting the most gorgeous / sought-after women / and luring them into my net / seducing them

just the idea of this has been driving me mad!

especially because i just got married / and i love my wife / i really do! in fact / i'm probably the luckiest man in the world / when i walk down the street with her on my arm / people look at me like they're thinking **my god** / **why is she with him? is he her father** / **what's so great about him?** to have met someone who i adore and can live with and who adores me and i . . . i . . . i mean she's not only gorgeous / she's brilliant she's incredibly bright / and together we've started a small business out of nothing! / which is a thrill / an absolute thrill and i mean / i . . . i . . . i wouldn't do anything to jeopardize this relationship / that's why i made a vow to myself to be faithful / i promised myself: *claude* / *you're not going to mess this one up* / i wouldn't want to do anything that could possibly hurt her / and yet i find myself going out for walks at night / wandering around the streets looking for these *ungettable* women / imagining animal conquests

i wake up in the morning in a cold sweat from an evening of fantasy and longing / my wife strokes my head / she gives me the sweetest little kiss / so sweet / so tender / i tell her i love her / i call her *coeur de ma vie* / *heart of my life* / i make love to her / moaning / whispering testaments of my

unwavering eternal devotion / i tell her i can't live without her
i tell her that i think of no one else but her / i lie to her / i lie
to myself / look / she's happy / i'm happy / i'm happy i'm
not alone / i'm happy i can lie to myself and tell myself i'm
happy i'm no longer a single man / she's happy thinking that
i think that she's happy / i lie / she lies / although she
may *actually* be happy (i doubt it though)

later in the evening after leaving the all-nude female review
i walk in a westerly direction / hurriedly / for three and a
quarter miles / mostly looking down towards the pavement
with thoughts of saving africa from drought and starvation
combined with ideas about seducing this coffee shop waitress
into a feast of sodomy and fresh lobster / i reach the west side
pier / for nine and a third minutes / i stare at the polluted
orange-purple sunset / take in one long very deep breath
then turn towards the east / unzip my pants and urinate
against the remaining shell of an abandoned dilapidated tow
truck / i walk twenty-three blocks to the resident hotel / take
the elevator up to my little room / my little s.r.o. on the
thirteenth floor / put the key in the door and turn the knob
my heart sinks / the room is smaller and stuffier than i
remember / there's barely enough space for the queen-size
bed and the bureau (which doubles as a desk) / books
magazines / and dirty clothes are stacked up against
the peeling pink wallpaper / down along the worn-out
carpeted floor a fly is making figure eights / diving in and
out of the remains of a canned minestrone soup
left open on the hot plate

under the blanket / an amorphous form: my wife *violaine*
is sleeping / i'm nauseous and afraid / afraid of the walls that
surround me / afraid of being choked by vows of marriage
and unrealistic expectations / the smell of sleep oozes from
the clump of blanket which is my new young bride / the walls

good advice

are parenthetical brackets surrounding negligible lives

off-the-cuff asides from the great life happening somewhere

outside / i lift open the window / stick my head out into the

night air and breathe / **the sky is teeming
with stars!** (not really / but for new york it's a lot of

stars / there are at least a half dozen stars out there) the moon

is almost full / or it had just been full / i'm not really sure

because you hardly ever see the sky in the city / there is no

sky in new york city / there are the tops of buildings / there's

uptown / the top floor / the penthouse / the dense canopy

of smog / the sound of planes overhead / but mostly there is

no sky / except for some reason / tonight / tonight / looking

out my window / the city is nothing but sky / the moon is

beautiful and brilliant / and it's up there in the sky / i wake

my wife *violaine* / *violaine sweetheart* / *come to the window
with me and see* / she clings to me at the window / together

we gaze at the silver moon / at the half dozen stars (delegates

from unseen constellations) the view from the window of

our little room is glorious / it's glorious! i love new york

oh how i love new york!

i've traveled throughout the world / i've been to the great cities

of the world: paris / moscow / london / marrakesh / beirut

jerusalem / bombay / cairo / and nothing / **nothing**

compares to new york! the buzzing lights / the storied

windows / the perfection of architectural chaos / the

honking / blaring / screeching / crashing sounds of traffic

a child screams / crickets throb the cool night air / and

somewhere / way out there in the far recesses of the sky

stars are colliding / new planets are being born as others die

nebulae explode spewing cosmic debris / the universe expands

in all directions / as violaine and i wrap around each other at

our little window / i love her / i tell her i love her so much

i'm so happy to be alive / to be with her at this moment / i

tell violaine *we may have a puny eleven-foot-square roach-
infested hotel room for a home* / *but we have this incredible view*

we have each other / we live only three and a quarter blocks

five and a half minutes from lincoln center / where we can go to

hear the greatest operas of all time / mozart / rossini / verdi

beethoven / performed by the greatest orchestra and the greatest

singers in the world / we're surrounded by the most international

the most intellectual / the most chic / vital / and important

people / and we are two amongst them / our work is important

it is completely original and fresh / we are alive in the most

radiant city during one of the great / perhaps the greatest

most pivotal moments in history

everything i say / i truly believe from the depths of my soul

the next morning i realize that it's a lie / it's all a lie / an

illusion / i'm lying to myself / i know that this is true / and

so i lie to myself some more / i tell myself *it's not a lie / i'm*

doing what i'm doing and it is important / it is valuable / it

is worthwhile / it is good / and i am the best at what i do

the best in the whole world!

it's not that i need to know that i'm the best / it's just that

i want to do my best / and i do love my wife / like no one

else in the whole world / and as for my insatiable desires

my ridiculous cruel fantasies / they're normal / and maybe

someday they'll go away / and even if they don't / i'm a

good person / a kind person / i'm a lucky person

a happy person / really! i am a very / very

happy / happy / person

for god's sake!

i could have found a cure for a.i.d.s. by now / instead i invented a new kind of jewelry / it's my revenge! they didn't want me / it's their loss / it's everybody's loss i had to go all the way down to the level of the damn streets bypass all the intermediaries / you can't sell a movie in the streets / you can't sell a cure for cancer in the streets / you can't revolutionize the study of human sexuality on a street corner / but you can sell earrings and broaches and necklaces out there / and make money off it **all you need is garbage** / if you are an alchemist / you don't need anything but garbage / other people's garbage / it's everywhere you know / garbage / garbage is everywhere! glass / metal / paper / all the necessary ingredients / and if you have a brain that is constantly pregnant with ideas you can figure out ingenious ways to take people's garbage transform it into jewelry (the likes of which nobody has ever seen before) and sell it back to them / that's what i do / i take your garbage / alchemize it into jewels and gems / and then you give me money so you can wear it around the streets because you think it makes you look cool

after my nightmare with medicine / i spent two years running around licking assholes and sucking toes in order to get funding to make a movie / then i practically had to go to bed with that seventy-five-year-old woman so she'd give me the money to start a charitable organization / i tried to get funding to bring refrigeration to poor people in morocco because when i was there i couldn't help but notice all the children getting sick from spoiled meat / i tried to bring medical supplies to jewish refusnicks in the soviet union so they could set up their own clinic / i tried to form a nonprofit company that created incentives for small businesses to export products overseas / i tried to start a magazine dedicated to keeping married couples sexually active (with each other) i tried to work within the system / i got my degrees in this that / and the other thing / **sure** / **i wanted to start at the top** / wouldn't you? with a mind like mine / wouldn't you expect to start at the top? i tried doing it by the book / i did everything you're supposed to do / i sent in my curriculum vitae / i made out proposals / i filled out the necessary forms / i learned the art of the pitch / i made sure always to get to the person in charge / which nine times out of ten was a man / and so i'd meet with the man / i'd pitch to the man / and he'd introduce me to another man and then another man / and they'd listen to my ideas and nod they'd look at all my plans and nod / they'd offer me a cigar nine times out of ten they offered me a cigar / and i'd say *no thanks* / and then they'd offer me a drink / and i'd say *no thanks* / we'd eat and we'd laugh and i'd talk and they'd nod and then we'd shake hands / that's right! nine times out of ten i shook hands with the man / i shook hands with the man's partner and the man's friend / **i shook a lot of hands** / and then i'd wait for a call / send a follow-up letter / then wait for a call / one week / two weeks / three weeks / not a ring / so i'd pick up the phone / i swallowed my pride a little / and i picked up the phone and dialed the number / and said *can i speak with . . .* and then they'd put me on hold / i'm on hold / i'm on hold / i'm on hold / and then i'd say *yes uh* / *can i please speak with mr. man?* and they'd say **well yeah** / **who may i say is calling?** and then it was nine times out of ten it was **well mr. man isn't in at the moment** / *well then can i leave a message?* **well why don't you just call back** / **call back** / **call back tomorrow**

striking gold

so you keep calling four five six seven eight nine ten times
a hundred times / a thousand times / **uh well mr. man is
not here at the moment** / **you might try to call him
back** / **not available at the moment** / **call him
back** / **call him back in an hour** / **he's in a meeting
in a conference** / **out to lunch** / **out of town** / **out
of the country** / until it's **mr. man is no longer in
no longer in our division** / **but feel free to try
again** / **try again in an hour** / **in a day** / **in a
month** / till it's **mr. man has been transferred
permanently transferred** / just like that / till finally
it's **mr. man is no longer employed in our
organization** / and that's how it went for two years
maybe three (i lost count) until one morning

i just woke up and said

to hell with mr. man!
i'm not going to lick mr. man's
ass anymore! i don't need
mr. man anymore!

now

you may be capable of licking mr. man's ass
in fact most people are very very very very very capable
very talented at doing that / that is why mr. man has got
himself a very licked ass / but not by me / not anymore
because that morning i just finally decided that i was through
waiting / there'll be no more waiting in my life / not for the
phone to ring / or the letter to come / or the handshake
i'm not waiting for mr. man or anybody else to tell me
whether it's yes or it's no or it's still maybe maybe maybe
maybe / unh unh / i don't need anybody else's approval
or disapproval / not from a bank or a foundation or a
congressman or a minister or an ambassador or a c.e.o. or
a billionaire or millionaire or even a clerk / never again
will i wait for anybody / other than myself

i am an orphan / i have the mentality of an orphan / i don't
have a family to run to for help / and if you go to strangers
asking for help they either want to screw you or screw you over
or they want you to chase after them all over the world / and
then they want nothing less from you than your blood / and
that if you ask me / *that* is prostitution / pure prostitution!
pure pure pure pure pure and simple

i tried to make a meaningful contribution / to use my brain
to improve human conditions / to better mankind / but no
one would have me / so i woke up one day and said
to hell with you / *to hell with them* / *to hell with*
everybody! from this point on i'm looking after
myself / *and my wife* / *and that's it*

i
tumbled
down
from
my
high
hopes
my high ideals / my highfalutin aspirations
i descended to the bottom / all the way to the bottom
into the garbage / and for the first time in my life

i looked around and everywhere i turned

beneath my feet were precious metals
radiant and shining gems
teeming / glorious / abundant
and there for the taking

strange apology

i have the right to attack you
but i don't have the right to go beyond
that point / i have the right to lash you with
my sharp tongue / but i don't
have the right to leave
you the way i did
promise to never let me leave you
again like that / promise me that!
because you're too important
you're too dear to me / i have the
right to attack you / i have the right
to complain / i have the right to
expect the impossible from you / but
it's not my place to judge you / to judge
you to the very core of your existence
it's not my place to minimize the
choices you make for your life

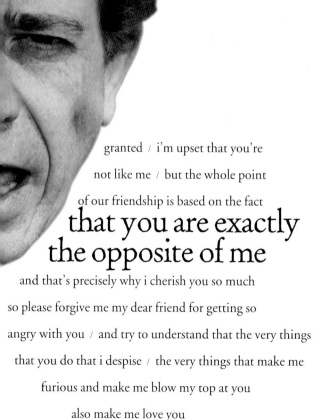

granted / i'm upset that you're

not like me / but the whole point

of our friendship is based on the fact

that you are exactly
the opposite of me

and that's precisely why i cherish you so much

so please forgive me my dear friend for getting so

angry with you / and try to understand that the very things

that you do that i despise / the very things that make me

furious and make me blow my top at you

also make me love you

love you all the more

big boss man

he took my hand and kissed it then he took the money he took his miserable forty-two dollars pay and spit on it

spitting on money is a form of gratefulness in russia / it's a gesture that means *may you always have good luck* / here is a man who doesn't speak a word of english / i pay him about five dollars something an hour / you know / a little more than minimum wage / i give him barely enough money to provide for his children / and he kisses my hand / this is how beholden one human being can become to another human being / if you give them work / if you give them a livelihood

at first / the way he treated me made me feel privileged to be of help to a man so eager to work / so appreciative of being in this country / i felt proud to contribute to his well-being / i felt good about providing work for all of my employees / i patted myself on the back / i thought to myself *making money is a good thing* / *you see* / *money isn't inherently bad* / *money isn't necessarily corrupting or evil a moral person* / *an honest person* / *can run a business* / *hire other people* / *so they can earn money too* / *it's an arrangement that benefits all parties: the employer* / *the employee* / *the distributor* / *the retailer* / *the consumer* / *the whole economy*

everybody makes out!

i gained no particular pleasure from seeing this man kiss my hand / none at all / what amazed me though / what took me by surprise was the strange and unfamiliar sensation of seeing a man / an older man / look into my eyes with an expression of sheer indebtedness / that's what got to me / that look of

if it weren't for you i don't know what i would do

for a brief moment i saw myself in a beneficent and honorable position / for one brief moment i forgot the legacy of my grandfather eugene debs / i forgot the awful / dangerous power of what it means to be a capitalist / for that moment i wished i had more money i could shower down on this guy i almost gave him an extra forty-two dollars / but then while saying good night at the elevator doors / i realized i wasn't doing him any great favor at all / in fact i was castrating him looking into his dark russian eyes / this obedient / overly appreciative hungry immigrant / helped me realize that this social contract was no more just or fair than the one he left behind / in the communist society he came from / there was no individual to bow down to / he involuntarily traded his self-respect to become a piece of the state / equal to everybody else / guaranteed a minimum level of bare-bones sustenance his imagination / dignity / and self-worth were sucked up by a bleak / rotting system / till finally he escaped / leaving behind his country / his friends / his home / his language he comes to america and is automatically castrated / by giving him forty-two dollars cash at the end of each day i castrate him whatever was left of his integrity is gone / as soon as my hand reaches out towards his / and his hand grabs hold of the forty-two dollars / the core of what makes him a sovereign human being is instantly massacred / standing by the elevator / we are not just two men saying good night / i am the boss and he is the employee / the slouch of his shoulders / the subtle nod of his head / and that look of indebtedness in his eyes / tell the whole story / that look in his eyes is imprinted in my mind as the elevator doors close / oh my god! he'll do almost anything to please me! suddenly the unspoken dynamic is crystal clear / the employee has a built-in sense of inferiority / while the boss feels superior this is the essence of capitalism / it is evil!

big boss man

under communism there is no well-being / under capitalism no solace / both are evil / one system can never work because it goes against human nature / the other is an exercise in castration / either way you lose / marx wanted everybody to be equal / but marx didn't realize that human beings are corrupt and power hungry **the voice of the people turned out to be a disaster!** of course russian communism wasn't really communism / it was a horror story / it was crap! human beings aren't ready for communism / not for another two thousand years at least / today / if you give everybody an equal share / nobody will do a thing / we're not evolved enough for true communism / we're still essentially brute animals with an instinct to kill / that instinct is the foundation of the capitalist system / it's a very very cruel arrangement under communism a worker probably feels like just one of millions / under capitalism he has the illusion of freedom but then the boss cuts off his wings / he can't fly / the boss paralyzes his instinct to dream / he doesn't follow his own dreams anymore / if you're the boss / he follows your dreams

how despicable i am for being a boss! as good and kind and generous as i am to my employees / as much as they act like they like me **they must hate me** / the more i think of ways to make their lives more pleasant / the more i shower them with gifts and bonuses and extra vacations the more they must resent me / by paying for all their medical expenses / by rounding a day's pay up to the nearest ten-dollar figure / by helping them with their english / by treating them like human beings / they must / underneath their smiles and expressions of gratitude / they must hate me a little / i can tell because of the look of astonishment in their faces whenever they receive an unexpected bonus / even though i am good to them they know that they are slaves / the animosity and distrust are built into the system / if they didn't hate me there would be absolutely no hope for them / the itsy bitsy teeny tiny remaining two percent of self-respect they have to keep their sanity they must use to hate me / so what do i do? i threaten to take away even that last remaining two percent of dignity / by being nice to them! / that's complete slavery!

if i was to recommend one thing to a fellow human being it would be to never never never never become an employee! at all costs / do not become an employee to another person even if you're penniless or you're sick / it's no excuse / no matter what your situation / you must figure out a way to work for yourself / be your own boss / and if you have to (for some reason) if you have to be an employee / then be an employee of the state / the faceless state / so you're not castrated by an individual person / so you don't have to become a slave to another human being / the fear of the boss is built into the system / it goes very very deep / it goes way back to fear of authority / fear of the teacher / the nun / the brother / the principal / the grown-up / it's practically the most unhealthy relationship you can have / you rent your life to this man (or this woman) he pays you a salary and in return you give him your life / in slavery the boss owned you / you belonged to him / in capitalism he rents you / by allowing your boss to rent half your waking life / he ends up owning you / he owns at least half your life / the other half you're tired / dejected / castrated / i.e. you've lost your life / so if you're going to live in this imperfect world / and you've got half a brain in your head / don't be a slave / you might as well live your life as the head of the company / the leader of the pack / you might as well be the castrating son of a bitch guy at the top / you might as well be *the big boss man*

.0001% of the time

seventy-three percent of the time you spend with judith and that's okay / **do i complain?** fourteen percent of the time you spend with your father and your mother and your brother / that's okay / **do i complain?** i don't complain / you can go and be with them as much as you want / thirteen percent of the time you go with harvey and you disappear from circulation / and i don't get to see you all that's left is .0001 percent of your time / i see you maybe ten minutes every month on average / and if i want to see you a little more / let's say twelve minutes a month / fifteen minutes a month / if i want to kiss your sweet face a little more / what do i have to do? **do i have to pay you?** is that what i have to do? alright / okay / i'll make you an offer / whatever price / whatever salary they pay you at that school you teach at / i'll double it / just tell me the price they pay you and i'll double it / whatever it is / just pack up your things / empty out your desk / and come and work for me / i'm begging you / i could use somebody with a brain to work for me / i know you probably won't go for it but think about it / okay?

look / you don't have to quit your job you don't have to quit hanging around with judith and harvey and dennis and charlie and your brother or any of your other friends / **i can live with .0001 percent** / **i can live with it** / i'm not complaining / **i can live with it!**

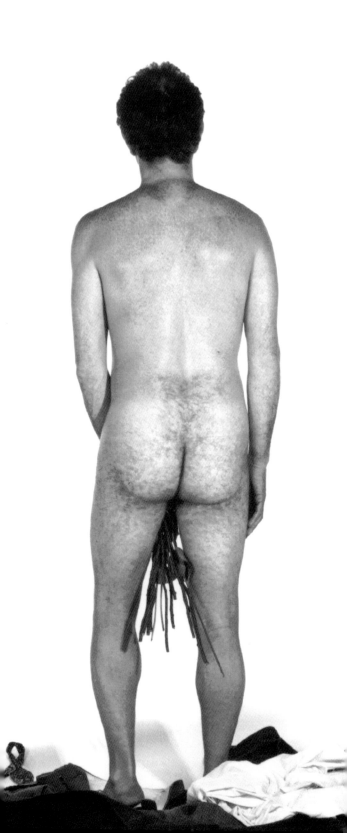

time and time again

i am appalled by your behavior!

when it is your job to remain neutral / you take sides / when your job is to back me up / back me up no matter what / you remain neutral / when your job is to laugh / you cower when you're supposed to be like stone / i hear you snicker through your teeth / if i am engaged in an argument / in a debate with someone else / your responsibility as a friend is to remain neutral / you cannot laugh and grin and sneer and make little noises / it is not your place to take sides / unless of course / unless you choose to back me up / if you must if you must take sides / **take sides with me!** but to take sides with my opponent / that my dear / my good old friend is the ultimate slap in the face / again and again and again / you prove yourself to be an absolute neanderthal / a caveman!

and i cannot
tolerate
that from you
any
longer

that man had a mediocre mind and i told him so / i don't care / i don't care how old he is / or how much music he has written / or what other people think or say about him i don't care what kind of a reputation he has! *bravo!*

everybody was on their feet applauding him *bravo bravo bravo!* why were they there in the first place? can you tell me that? why were they cheering him on so? i know why / i know why / it's because / because **the new york times said to** / because the pundits / the bandits of the public mind said that he was next in line for their attention and their praise / that's why! and in that whole mob of obedient soldiers / i was the only dissenting voice / i was the only one who dared to speak the truth / and you / with all your talk of civil rights and freedom of speech / you with your bleeding heart for the underdog and the downtrodden / you of all people / you should've been proud that it was your friend / your best friend who was the only one who didn't bow down to the consensus of the crowd it was your friend who retained his independence of thought your friend and no one else / the least you could have done is have respect for my minority of one / but no not you! what did you do?

you sided with him!

yeah yeah / i know i know / you have your reasons for you / just because it's something *new* / because it's *in-no-vative* / because it's *avant-garde* / you're blinded to the fact that there is **not an iota** / **not a nose hair** / **not a mole spore of human emotion in that man's work!** look / i understand your need to blindly march into the hip halls of vacant trend and fashion irrespective of quality or taste / okay / okay / you have the right to your opinion believe me / if it was the other way around / if you stood there the only one applauding / a crowd of angry faces scowling at you disapprovingly / booing voices all around you / i would be there by your side / i would have listened to your argument with respect / even if i despised the work

time and time again

(as i did) i would have backed you up all the way / that is the
measure of my friendship / but alright / okay / you're
different / you are you and all i expect from you now is

an apology

time and time again you do this to me / and you have
never / never / you have never ever ever ever
ever apologized / not to me / not
to anyone / but now it's time for you to begin / and if you
don't want to apologize / because / of course you'll have
all your excuses and rationales and attacks and all kinds of
twisted reasons to give me why you did nothing wrong / why
it was me who acted poorly / why it was me who embarrassed
you in front of your brother and all your other so-called
friends / if that's your choice / if you do choose not
to apologize / then i will have to do what your
mother did / i'll just have to

punish you

because that is the only approach / that is the only thing you
know how to respond to: *punishment* / i will *punish you*
punish you / *punish you* / i will *punish you*
with silence

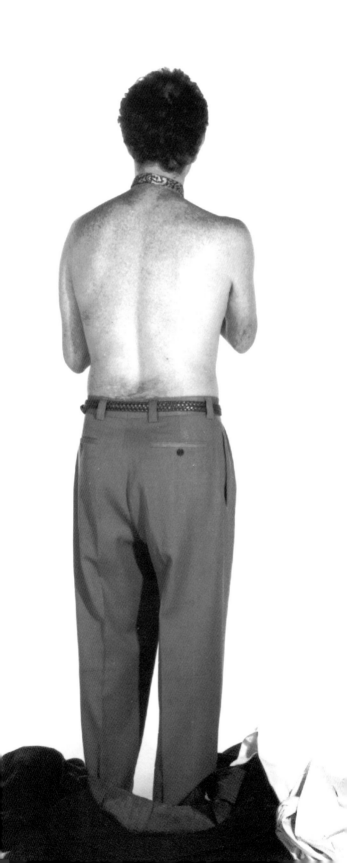

the lie revisited

it's sad / very sad

not for me / i've lived a good life

i've lived at least a dozen lives in this short life

it's only sad when i think of my wife violaine / it's / it's

unfair! i don't want to slow her down / she's on her way

up / and that's all she should be concerned with / going

forward / i tell her *i'm just the first of your many husbands*

but she doesn't like to hear that / she hates when i say that!

she'll get over me / after the initial shock / she's strong / she's

incredibly strong / **you're a walking time**

bomb / that's what the doctor told me just yesterday

the nurse left a message saying it was urgent i call back right

away / it's a good thing violaine is out of town / when i

called my doctor back he sounded almost frantic / which is

very unprofessional don't you think? a doctor / you want

a doctor to be cool and in control / you don't want an

emotional doctor / he said he never saw a cholesterol count

as high as 320 on a person my age / he said as far as he

knows i might have one of the highest cholesterol counts in

the history of new york city / which is a very high cholesterol

city / **you're a walking time bomb** / that's

what he told me / he wants me to come in to the office for

more tests first thing monday morning / he wants to start

giving me drugs and . . . and . . . you can imagine the things

he'd like to do to me / these cardiovascular guys / they act like

they know what they're doing / now they're into angioplasty

that's their latest gimmick / these guys are

clowns! they're high-priced clowns playing with

balloons / they don't know what they're doing / they're toying

with people's lives! he can't do anything for me / i have a

special condition: *genetic hyper-cholesterinia* / a genetic

disorder that can't be helped / there's nothing medicine can

do for it / . . . diet? what about diet? i already cut all fats out

of my diet ten years ago / all i eat is vegetables and fish / it

doesn't make a bit of difference / the cholesterol just keeps

going up and up and up / . . . stress? what about stress? i

won't do anything for my stress / **i live for stress**

i thrive on stress / **i am stress!**

i'd rather die than be at peace / the thought of being tranquil

makes me nervous / very nervous / if i woke up tomorrow

morning and felt sedate or blissed out / that would kill me

that's what would kill me / . . . scared? **i'm not**

scared / i've lived a good life / a full life / i'm a little

sad that's all / not on my behalf / i'm sad for violaine / i won't

tell her though / there's no reason to scare her / she already

knows i have a cholesterol problem / there's no reason

to tell her that i'm a walking time bomb

---

it's been five years since i explained to you my theory on

lying – the correlation between the lie and happiness / and

over these five years not much has changed / and everything

has changed! i am still an extraordinarily happy man / even

more than i was then / i'm probably one of the happiest

people alive today / i still consider myself a very honest man

and i still use the lie technique on a daily basis / but it's

changed / the lie isn't a structural thing anymore

today it's more of an embellishment

five years ago we started a tiny little business / today it's

grown to a half-million-dollar enterprise / although we're still

living and working out of the same resident hotel / instead

of just one single room we rent the whole floor! we also

own three apartments in paris / we travel all over the world

(separately / that way someone's always here looking after the business / as a matter of fact violaine has been in hawaii

for two weeks now / i just got a fax from her a half hour ago

saying she still hasn't been able to get out to see the ocean

she faxes me two / sometimes three times a day) five years ago

when we got married our love was based on a very powerful

attraction / like most new couples our love was mostly an

illusion / a dream / a fantasy / today our love is a reality!

you marry somebody for better or worse / and ninety percent

of the time it's for worse / but i got lucky / she was just a girl

when i married her / today she's an amazing woman / every

woman i was ever with turned out to be so difficult / so

complicated / sure in the beginning everything seems light

and breezy / but that feeling always turned out to be just the

endorphins dancing around on the head of a pin / it wasn't

the woman / it wasn't me / after a year or two we were at

each other's throats / but with violaine it's completely different

you know me / **i'm in an argument with**

the whole world / i argue with everyone except

for violaine / we don't argue / it astonishes me / all the little

obnoxious things that go hand in hand with running a business

with living in new york / with being married / being alive

all the horrible little nuisances and disappointments / they

don't bother her / she's a phenomena / she's so *undifficult*

i am an oozing / festering / open wound and violaine is like

the oil / she is the lubricant that makes the whole thing

bearable / my only argument with her is that i'm the first of

her many husbands / this is a daily argument! why shouldn't

other human beings have the chance to taste such happiness?

that i should have her all to myself doesn't make any sense

it doesn't seem fair to me / with violaine i feel like i have

discovered a natural antidote to life's harsh / prickly realities

and like a scientist / i should be able to publish my findings

i want to publish my wife! i know it

sounds strange but that to me would be the unselfish thing to

do / to publish my wife / and then i should win the nobel

prize for such a discovery / i should be able to say to the world

look! look!
look what i've found!
go ahead

put it through the rigors of scientific analysis
do your double-blind studies / be my guest / come!
study! partake in the secret to a happy life!

but that's not the way things work / it makes no sense to me

if i discovered a cure for a.i.d.s. or cancer / i'd get locked up

if i didn't share my discovery / if i kept it to myself

that's why i say the lie is no longer a structural imperative

for me / my love for my wife is as solid and as real as a rock

it's real! the success of my business is no longer in need

of illusion or make-believe / the success is a structural reality

today / the use of the lie is only needed for enhancement

think of it like a fire / five years ago i needed to construct the

fire practically from scratch every day / i would bring my wife

imaginary logs in order to build the illusion of a fire / flowers

candles / nightgowns / endless pronouncements of love

all of that would help build the fire / i would tell myself that

our new business / this endeavor / after all the projects i've

undertaken / after all the projects and careers i've had to abort

this one / this one will be the one that will succeed / i lied to

myself in order to believe in something / in order to keep

going / i lied to my employees / i tried to create the illusion

that we were more than just a hand-to-mouth operation

working out of one room in a welfare hotel / five years ago

the lie created an illusion that things were secure / that i was

in love / it made everyone around me feel secure and loved

but then the illusion became a reality / that is what happened

in five short years / but still / the happiness needs to be

the lie revisited

sustained / you can't just go on being happy like this / it's
it's unnatural / so in order to sustain the happiness you have
to bring a piece of wood to the fire / you lie a little bit / just
to keep it going / you don't have to build the fire from scratch
it's already there / you just do what you have to do
to keep it from burning out

here i am / for a moment off to the side looking at my life
i wonder: *now that i'm a walking time bomb / will the fires go
out? am i near the time when i'll no longer be able to feed the
fire with my little logs? my little lies? and when that day comes
when i'm no longer around to stoke the flames or blow the embers
will they be able to sustain themselves without me?
that will be the measure of my success!*

what i told you before about one of us needing to stay in
new york to look after the business while the other one travels
well that's true but it's also a little bit of a lie / one of the
reasons violaine and i travel separately is to sustain sexual
desire between us / after three or four years of marriage i
started feeling the same pattern of hormonal disinterest i felt
years ago with my first wife marizette / and yet the love i have
for violaine is so strong / i couldn't bear the idea of losing her
i had to figure out a way to keep the endorphins alive between
us / i came across a series of studies done on rats / in these
studies scientists observed that male rats repeatedly lost interest
in the female rats they were paired with after some period of
time together / then they separated the male and female rat
by a wall with airholes in it / after they lifted the wall the male
still had no interest in mating with the female / but then they
discovered if they closed up the holes / and separated them
for just a day or two / the male got all excited when he was
reunited with his partner / they screwed like crazy / it turns
out that rats are not the only species with this behavior pattern
in many many species the male is excited by the smell of all

the other females of the world except his own mate's / sex specialists are so stupid! they continue to get it wrong time and time again / the solution to this problem has been sitting there right under their noses and they still can't see it / the solution is so simple:

get away from each other!

there is a gland called the sebaceous gland that releases chemicals on the surface of the skin / it produces an odor and other very subtle secretions along the skin / at first the attraction to these secretions is very very high / then after a period of time together your partner's secretions get all over you / they're in the air / they're on the furniture and the towels / they're on every article of clothing in your house there is no longer a sensation of *other* / the more you're swimming constantly in your partner's sebaceous secretions the more neutralized they become / so naturally you're attracted to the secretions of anybody else besides your mate's that's why you have to get away from each other / but it can't just be for a day or two / in humans the detoxification period is at least three to four weeks / and both partners have to get away / if one partner stays home and the other travels / the partner at home is still surrounded by all the same sebaceous secretions / so what we do: violaine goes away for two or three weeks to hawaii or san francisco / and then i go away for two or three weeks to africa or russia or someplace / and then when we get together we have the most passionate sex i've ever had in my entire life / the sebaceous gland secretions work as though we're strangers / and yet we don't have to fantasize about anyone or anything else because we already love each other we indulge in the pleasures of rediscovering one another / for about two days / we lick and smell and tickle and peel and rip each other's clothes off as if we're brand-new lovers / to cup

the lie revisited

my hand on her breast / the breast of the woman i adore

more than anyone in the world / to feel her fingers running

through my hair is for a few days a new thrill / we go crazy

over each other / *we make believe* / then we settle down into

our affectionate caring / loving / working / but typically

asexual pattern of living / then after a few months we each go

away and then we come back and it's all gangbusters and

passion for a day and a half / two days / and so together we

lie a little bit / we each bring a log to the fire to keep warm

it's such an elegant solution!

before i die i'd like to publish the results of our marriage

if people practiced this method / i'd guarantee

the divorce rate would plummet

so we do what we have to do to keep our precious love alive

we lie a little / we make believe a little / actually there's a lot

of little lying going on / for instance / i told you that violaine

is at an international trade show in hawaii for three weeks

what i didn't tell you is that she is sharing a room with a man

a gorgeous blonde blue-eyed divorced man about her age

who she likes very much / he's also in the accessory business

she knows him from switzerland and so we decided for her

protection and to save a little money / they should share

a room in the hotel together / they also most likely dine

together every night / and have breakfast together every

morning / and well / i am a human being / i am a man

and so i have my jealousies / i have my fears about the two

of them / i want to pick up the phone and call her and say

something like *and how's maurice?* / *are the two of you getting*

along okay? maybe say something a little sarcastic / something

so she could react and i could tell by the inflection of her voice

whether she's overreacting / or trying to be nonchalant about

him / anything just to get a hint of what is going on / but i

don't pick up the phone / and when she calls me / i don't ever

mention maurice / or ask about maurice / or ask what she is

doing with her free time / because my insecurity could create

something from nothing / the truth is probably that nothing

nothing is going on at all / and the fantasy / the lie

spinning around in my head could plant the seed of something

that could grow to become the truth / you don't plant a seed

in fertile ground unless you want something to grow there

it's enough that she's in hawaii / one of the most romantic

spots on earth / sleeping in the same room with an unmarried

eligible hunk of a guy / without me calling up and

planting a seed in the middle of that

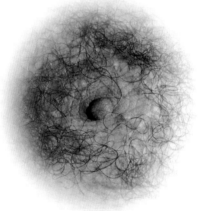

every human being on the surface of this planet

every human being would say something / except claude

claude looks at the situation and says *i love her* / *i want her*

to have an orgasm with this man / *i want her to experience the*

joys of the flesh / *and when she returns i will double* / *triple my*

attentions towards her / *so that i could earn her love all over*

again / *i will try so hard to please her* / *to make her so happy*

that she will stay with me and be devoted to me till the day i die

nobody / i don't care how young he is

or tall or swiss or charming / **nobody**

could make her as happy as i do / so i lie by not

revealing the jealousy that consumes me / again the lie

becomes a tool for happiness / i also lie to myself because i

don't want to face the truth that i am indeed a very jealous man

after all / i am supposed to be a pioneer

of human sexuality for god's sake!

i am claude! and yet i want to call her and say

what the hell are you two doing?

but i don't / i let her enjoy her sensuality / i catapult myself two thousand years from now when people finally reach the level of consciousness beyond fears and jealousy / when women are free to enjoy their sexuality without being tied down to this ancient notion called fidelity / i imagine myself to be the claude of the year 4000 / it's a better claude than the jealous claude of today / the claude of 4000 doesn't need to be possessive / the claude of 4000 wants his wife to experience every kind of man / tall / black / fat / swiss / aborigine every kind of man she might desire (or woman for that matter) after all / i cherish the fact that i've had sex with so many women / at the moment of my last breath of life i will thank god for all the sex i've had / after all / if it was good for me why shouldn't my wife experience the good things in life too? anything less than that would be a double standard / except the truth is / the truth is i would be devastated if i found out that violaine had sex with maurice / because i'm not the claude of 4000! i am only the claude of the late twentieth century / my heart and my brain are still at odds / so i have to lie to my wife to conceal the insecurity and the fatigue that comes from the fight between my brain and my heart

it drains me / it saps me of my energy / because

the truth is (and this is hard for me to admit) the truth is

every second since she's been in hawaii every sleepless moment i have been inside that hotel room / with the two of them / when i'm working / when i'm on the toilet / when i'm inside a movie theater in the middle of the day trying to take my mind off them / i am there inside that hotel room / i am right there with the two of them / but when i see her / when

i pick her up at the airport / i will lie / i will smile / i will shower her with kisses / i'll ask her how the show went while my tongue wants to scream

what have you been doing with maurice?

even if she mentions maurice in passing / i'll brush it off as if i'm completely indifferent / although too much disinterest could make her think that something's going on / so i'll show some concern for how well he did or didn't do at the show

i'll ask about his business / it's so un-american you know americans want to vomit up every nuance of emotion / every nagging doubt or suspicion / i am more british in this way i'm more like a wasp / show nothing / reveal nothing / it was the british who came up with the expression *certain things are better left unsaid* / of course they don't really live by it / they end up saying it all anyway / it just comes out in dribs and drabs / **but i live by this!** certain emotions will never leak out of me / which is not particularly french either / the french are more like americans / they just give it to you

the way i see it / the human spirit is like a bonsai tree you don't prune it with a mechanical object / that's too crude it will destroy the soul of the tree / you must prune with your fingers / very very delicately / and what you take away is as important as what you leave alone / you know / as much as i like to think of myself as the master pruner within my marriage / i know that is a lie / it's an illusion that makes me feel more in control / the truth is violaine lies to me on a daily basis as well / she's an extremely careful pruner that woman she could teach a course on concealment / particularly when

the lie revisited

it comes to bad news / she's a pro! she will keep any piece of bad news from me for as long as she can / and when she finally has to give me the bad news / she always wraps it in chocolate so that it doesn't taste so bad / **that's why i want to share her with the rest of the world!** she'll never tell me what she's really thinking (which is very swiss you know / she's so swiss) for instance / if i'm up all night in the studio working on a new invention / a new product / in the morning when i show her what i've done she always says she loves it / even if she hates it / at first i just thought that she was easy to please / until i discovered how good she is at lying / i finally realized that only ten yeses actually means yes / so now when i come to her and she tells me she loves something / i ask her *are you sure?* and she says **yes** / and i say *do you really mean it?* and if she says **yes yes yes yes yes yes yes yes yes** / if it's only nine yeses then that means she hates it / it's got to be ten yeses before i really know she loves it / of course i never told her i figured this out about her / because then i would have no way of knowing when a yes was really a yes / **everyone should live with a person who only says yes!** this is a very contrary and contentious world we're living in / and to wake up to the sound of a yes / and to go to sleep to the sound of a yes is very lubricating / even if you know that it's really a no / because you know that she says yes because she loves you / because she doesn't want to hurt you / so you make believe / you think the nine yeses are really nine yeses because you know that that's not what's really important / which is why at this moment in my life i have nothing to complain about / because probably for the first time in my life i've come to know what's really important now that i'm a ticking time bomb my life is filled with yeses!

i am the living proof that a man can really change / fifteen years ago i put the question to my first wife / i asked her *marizette* / *what would you do if i died?* her answer was *well* / she thought about it for a while / and she said *well i would be very upset at first* / *naturally* / *but i would get through it* / *because i'm a survivor* / then she said *eventually i suspect i would get back on my feet and meet other people* / *and i imagine one day i'd remarry* her response took me by surprise / actually i was devastated i expected her to say *if you die* / *i'll commit suicide! there would be no reason for me to live if you died* but she didn't say that / i was so upset / i became deranged for six days i wandered the streets dumbfounded and lost / it was shocking to realize that i had married someone who didn't feel the same way i did / but now / fifteen years later / my attitude has changed / i'm practically an old man next to my young wife / that's why i keep telling her that she will have a life after me / of course her reaction is always *no claude there'll never be anyone else but you* / but then i press her until she concedes *okay claude maybe one day i'll find someone* / *but i will never find anyone as brilliant as you* and my answer to her is *you're absolutely right* / *you won't! but now that you're an independent* / *powerful woman* / *you can marry a complete dodo bird and it wouldn't hamper you in any way* / you see! the idea of violaine being married to another man after i'm dead hardly bothers me at all

can you believe how much a man can change in fifteen years? can you believe it?

of course if *she* died i would be devastated / i think i would just drop dead on the spot / i would be so pathetic / because what would i do? go around looking to screw every woman i see? i wouldn't want to do that again / i'd kill myself first or just dry up like a branch on a tree and fall to the ground either that or i'd explode like a bomb / a ticking time bomb whose time has come and gone

call a spade a spade

a whole book warren

you write a whole book on me and you leave out

the most important word / how many times do you have

the word penis in this book? how many times?

count them / *penis penis penis penis penis penis penis* / but

not once / **not once** did you use the word *genius*

everybody who knows me calls me a genius / my employees

call me a genius / my clients call me a genius / my wife

even my neighbors call me a genius / but my best

friend who writes a book about me / he never

calls me a genius / you're the only one warren

you're the only one who refuses to call me a

genius / you think it looks bad / you think it

will make me look vain / i don't care what

anybody thinks about me / i have nothing

but utter contempt for the public

you know that i am completely anonymous in my business

my name doesn't appear on any of my inventions / i'm not on

the letterhead / i'm not in the brochures / i'm invisible / all

credit goes to the president of the company – my wife violaine

she gets all the credit! why? because i don't need to hear

the applause of miserable insect brains / i don't care what they

think about me / only my very select circle of friends know

my genius / a rock is a rock / a tree is a tree / a house is

a house / and a genius is a genius / let's call a spade a spade

what's wrong with calling yourself a genius? don't you think

mozart knew he was a genius? it's not vanity / mozart / rilke

and goethe all boasted that they were geniuses / that their

heated lust burned from both ends / from their penises as

well as their brains / on a daily basis! often on an hourly basis

whether i am a genius or not isn't the issue / the fact is that

the candle is burning at both ends

when it comes to my accomplishments and inventions you use

words like *brilliant* / *intelligent* / *ingenious* / *endowed with*

a penetrating intellect / you beat around the bush / when it

comes to sex you didn't say *intercourse* or *copulation* or *mating*

you said *fucking* or *screwing* or *having sex* / you didn't hedge!

how many people do you know in your life? a hundred? two

hundred? a thousand? and out of all these people that you

know / how many of them would you call a genius?

hello?
how many?
how many?

that's right!

so what's wrong with calling a spade a spade?

every day i come up with something brilliant! there's a chef

here in new york who wants to invest seventy-five thousand

dollars in our company / he's not a rich man / but he wants

to invest most of his money in me / why? because two weeks

ago i came up with a new way to make cheese / a month ago

i hardly knew the first thing about cheese / two weeks later

i'm inventing a whole new species of cheese / this man was

totally totally amazed / can you believe it? cheese!

why don't you put me in a series with nobel prize winners?

you say extraordinary ordinary people / that's your thesis

right? i have no problem with extraordinary / but i can't

remember anyone ever calling me ordinary / a genius is not

an ordinary person / i know i know / you think i'm pompous

well you're right / i am pompous! because that's what it takes

call a spade a spade

every day at four o'clock in the morning i look at myself in the mirror and say *wow!*

this is an incredible brain!

and the more i say it the more i am sinfully and totally arrogant / the more something ignites in my brain like a powerful supernova all my neurons catch fire at the same time / *that* is the moment of creativity / the moment of invention / the moment of genius / the first four or five times i experienced a total supernova like that / it changed the direction of my life dramatically / since then i've figured out a way to induce that state as a matter of course / as a way of living / *that's* what i want you to convey to your readers / if you tell them anything with this book i want you to tell them not just that i am a genius / but that everyone else / anyone who figures out how to control the power of the brain can be a genius too!

there are so many scientists today doing brain research neurobiologists / neurosurgeons / psychiatrists / but they are (for the most part) linear thinkers / they look at the brain through tunnel vision / like gardeners with their heads in the dirt / planting row after row of flowers / never really understanding the flower from the inside out

i am the flower!

if you want to understand me / if you want to understand the essence of who i am / then you've got to understand the anatomy of the creative process itself / you see / i believe

there is a rare transmitter in the neuron synapses of the brain

called *creative x* / and that transmitter only gets released

under extreme conditions such as a physical crisis or fatigue

or the imminence of death / for instance / if you walk into

a room and all of a sudden you see someone falling out of a

window / somehow you will find it in yourself to summon

up the strength to pull that person back into the room / now

normally you might not have that kind of strength / maybe

you've got a herniated disk in your back / or you're out of

shape / or overweight / maybe you're just very very lazy

but in a crisis situation you will most likely react like a

superhuman being and save the person's life *no matter what!*

extraordinary circumstances yield extraordinary strength of

the body / this is a documented fact! the same is true with the

brain / i'm sure you've heard testimonials from people with

near-death experiences / people who have come right up to

the end of their life **almost died** / in some cases

actually clinically died / then came back and lived to tell

very similar stories about the sensation of losing all their fears

entering an open transcendent space that is warm and filled

with a feeling of oneness with the universe and bathed in an

all-encompassing white light / and then afterwards all these

people changed their lives dramatically / most of them

attribute it to a religious experience or enlightenment / but

what it really is / is the brain faced with the absolute ultimate

crisis: **its own extinction** / and so it reacts in

an extraordinary way / that is the state i'm talking about!

that is the level of crisis that must be induced in order to

transform the *creative x* transmitters into an idea

who cares about the story of my life? really / nobody cares

about that! and i don't blame them / people are busy / if you

want to give your readers a flower / a real gift that they can use

to free themselves of their insect lives / to wake up the sleeping geniuses inside them / then print this up and make it

the last chapter of the book:

IGNITING THE
CREATIVE X TRANSMITTER
THE METHOD™

first you must isolate yourself from other human beings

then you need to deprive yourself of sleep for four or five

nights in a row so that you induce a state of extreme fatigue

so that you become like a zombie / you reach a state of

zombiehood / which is like your brain going haywire / your

thoughts simply collapse in on themselves / they're there and

then they're gone / what you hear / what you smell / what

you see / comes in a flash / then disappears / you're there

without being there / you're in a state of nowhere / it's like

a state of perpetual dying / then once in that state you need

to look in the mirror and tell yourself that you're a genius

the most incredible genius
in the whole world!

you must do this with total unequivocal conviction / and

then eventually it will happen / the combination of sheer

exhaustion and emphasizing the idea that you expect

something from your brain / screaming inside your mind

over and over again that you are a genius / creates a crisis

of saturation / lo and behold: *the creative x transmitter*

jumps over an unsuspecting synapse and ignites billions and

billions of electrons enveloping the entire electromagnetic

fields of the cortical and limbic systems / straight into the

amygdala (the center of the brain which is like the cauldron

where the intellect and the emotions come together) causing

an eruption comparable to the force of an exploding sun / the

discrete compartments of your brain then meld into one

harmonious organism / catapulting dormant electrons out

of their cubbyholes like triple-jointed trapeze artists / leaping

with abandon over faceless synapses / through each atom of

the brain / then down your arms and legs / out through your fingers and toes / and then back again / from out of a torpid state of zombiehood you look up and there before your eyes is

the answer! the solution! or just the seed of an idea that will change your life / it's an unbelievable feeling this feeling

it's beyond any analytical process / it's beyond anything you can learn in school or from a book / and usually it happens somewhere between four and five o'clock in the morning

there is probably no limit to what the brain can take on i suppose you can use this method to get your kitchen table to fly / or mobilize your T cells to destroy a terminal cancer but it's much easier (in terms of results) to get the brain to control the brain / believe me! the brain controlling the brain and the result being an idea is a snap compared to the brain controlling your kitchen table or your body against cancer

just this morning in fact / at five a.m. / i figured out a way to make candles out of spent motor oil! the guy at the service station down the block laughed at me when i asked him for the old oil / he thought it was such a joke **here! take all of it / we've got two barrels full out back ha ha he ho ha ha** / for five days i wracked my brain trying to figure out what to do with all this discarded grease then finally / early this morning i discovered that although the combustion level of the oil had been depreciated / i could still paraffinalize it back to an active state by mixing it with several different types of acetates / calciums / and carbons / and then by adding solidifiers and pouring it into a mold (of any shape or size) i could transform the dead oil into gorgeous wax candles / candles! which in turn should translate into an extra half-million dollars in sales for our business by the end of the year / not to mention less wasted oil and more light and romance to go around

call a spade a spade

maybe before i die / my last contribution to this earth will be to start a brain club / *The Brain Club*™ / i'll start out by getting twenty kids / dropouts from the most run-down neighborhood in the city / take them out of that environment and isolate them for six months / deprive them of sleep / and the usual distractions (drugs / television / gangs) and just have them scream into walls and walls of mirrors that they are geniuses and that they are capable of anything / and see what happens / it's not just a matter of saying *yes i can* / that is a passive approach / what i'm talking about is a state of great stress / like working out in a gym day after day / exercising a muscle needed to pull a person up from the window / only that muscle is your brain / you're pulling something up from your brain and it ignites / and before you know it / you're inventing something / you shouldn't be afraid to pump your muscle / that's what it takes / pump it! pump it for all you've got / look at yourself in the mirror and call a spade a spade / i am a genius / you are a genius / we've all got three billion unused cells inside our brains waiting to burst out waiting to be put to good use / nobody should think of themselves as ordinary / ordinary! i hate that! when i hear someone say (with pride people say this) *i am just an ordinary guy* / i don't understand it / what kind of an attitude is that to have about yourself?

listen / i don't care what you put in the book / i'm sorry warren / i hope you win a pulitzer prize for this book / i really do! regardless of whether or not you choose to use the G word you deserve to win a thousand awards for these books / that's what i wish for you / nothing less / but the truth is books come and go these days / they're a dime a dozen / a flash in the pan / i want you to do something for me that will last a really long time / okay? promise me that when i die you'll put up a monument or a tombstone with my favorite saying inscribed as an epitaph / will you do that for me? you know

i used to want to be cremated and have my ashes thrown
into the fountain at lincoln center / then for the longest time
i figured i'd jump off the balcony at the metropolitan opera
and land right on the stage splat just like that
i think everyone who loves the opera wants to die that way
because there are certain moments in certain operas that are so
sublime / you feel like you're at one with the whole universe
you just want to end it right there / but then about eight years
ago this old man actually did it! he jumped off the second-tier
balcony of the met and died right there on the stage / in the
middle of *la bohème* / everybody heard about it / it was such
a great death! the son of a gun took it from all of us / so now
i just want a tombstone / i don't care what you do with my
body / just make sure there's a simple tombstone / no names
no dates / no cupids / just this one sentence that i have lived
by since the age of thirteen when i left my parents

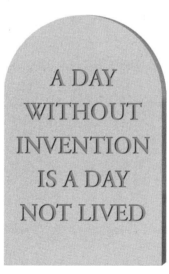

A DAY
WITHOUT
INVENTION
IS A DAY
NOT LIVED

this thought has been my survival kit my whole life / this
sentence / if you really want to understand me / forget about
everything else i told you / who needs 253 pages of verbal
diarrhea / throw it all out / and just keep this one simple
thought / that's all you need / that's my portrait!

This book was printed by offset lithography
on acid-free paper. All prepress work was composed
by Warren Lehrer on Macintosh computers using
Adobe Photoshop, Aldus PageMaker, Quark Express,
Aldus Freehand, and TypeStyler. The primary type
family used for the voice of Claude is Garamond,
based on the original design by Claude Garamond.
ITC Clearface is the principal text face used for
the introductory and back-matter pages. Over
two dozen other typefaces are used
throughout the book as well.

Many, many thanks to

my wife, Judith Sloan, for her encouragement, assistance, and wisdom; my editors, Sharon Dahl and Patricia Draher, for their tireless insight and care; Sally Brunsman, Kim Barnett, Philip Kovacevich, Sharon Rose Vonasch, and all the people at Bay Press for believing in me and making this implausible project a reality; my agent, Donald Farber, for separating good from evil spirits; and the New York State Council on the Arts, New York State Foundation for the Arts, and the Purchase College Association for their financial support. Also, special thanks to Jim Frank, Joan Lyons and the Visual Studies Workshop, Ruth and Arthur Lehrer, Vicki Dennis, Brian Lehrer, Clifton Meador, Phil Zimmermann, Lesley Stone, Rod Richardson, Margot Lovejoy, Leonard Seastone, Brad Freeman, and Violaine Galland for all their help. Most of all, I want to thank Claude Debs for being himself.

Warren Lehrer

is a writer, artist, performer, and book designer who celebrates the music of thought and speech, the complexity of personality, and the fine line between humor and tragedy. Acclaimed as "one of the most imaginative book artists of our time," Lehrer is known as a pioneer in the burgeoning field of visual literature. His previous books include *GRRRHHHH: a study of social patterns*, *FRENCH FRIES, i mean you know*, and *versations*. Lehrer's plays include *The Basic Training of Eugene Solomon*, cowritten with Dennis Bernstein, and *Denial of the Fittest* and *A Tattle Tale*, cowritten with his wife, Judith Sloan. Lehrer and Sloan also coproduced the weekly satirical radio segment *The Whole K'Cuffin World Report* for Pacifica Radio. With Harvey Goldman, Lehrer composed a contemporary opera entitled *The Search for IT and Other Pronouns*. His books have been exhibited internationally and are in the collections of major museums. He has received grants from the National Endowment for the Arts, the New York State Council on the Arts, the New York Foundation for the Arts, and the Ford Foundation as well as numerous awards, including three American Institute for Graphic Arts Book Awards and the International Book Design Award. Lehrer lives in New York City and teaches at the State University of New York at Purchase. He is presently working on **The Portrait Series** books based on women.